Notice to the Reader Upon Entering This Book

In this concoction, Marcel Proust's enormous work is alternately referred to as either *A la recherche du temps perdu*, *In Search of Lost Time*, *Remembrance of Things Past*, or simply *Remembrance*. In each case it is the same damn book.

He used to tell his story to every stranger that arrived at Mr. Doolittle's Hotel. He was observed at first to vary on some points, every time he told it, which was doubtless owing to his having so recently awaked.
—Washington Irving, "Rip Van Winkle"

*And those who live the secret wrong and badly
... lose it only for themselves and still hand it on,
like a sealed letter, without knowing it.*
—Rainer Maria Rilke,
Letters to a Young Poet,
July 16, 1903

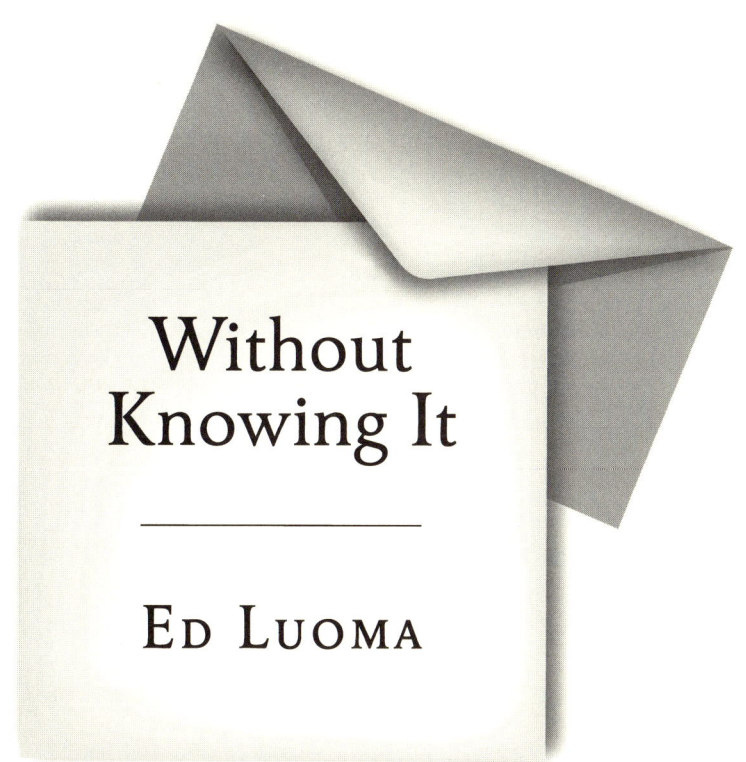

Without Knowing It

Ed Luoma

READERS' FORUM
WAYNE, PENNSYLVANIA

Copyright © 2007 by Ed Luoma

All Rights Reserved

No part of this book may be reproduced in any form or by any electronic or mechanical means including information storage and retrieval systems without permission in writing from the author, except by a reviewer who may quote brief passages in a review.

Manufactured in the United States of America

First Edition, 2007

Interior design: Rachel Reiss

PERMISSIONS

Remembrance of Things Past by Marcel Proust, transl. by C.K. Moncrieff and T. Kilmartin, copyright 1924, 1925, 1927, 1929, 1930, 1932 and renewed 1952, 1953, 1955, 1957, 1958, 1960 by Random House, Inc.

Excerpt from *Letters to a Young Poet* by Rainer Maria Rilke, transl. by M.D. Herter, copyright 1934 by W.W. Norton and Company, Inc. Reprinted by permission.

Buddhism Without Beliefs by Stephen Batchelor, copyright 1997 by Stephen Batchelor and The Buddhist Ray, Inc. Used by permission of Riverhead Books, an imprint of Penguin Group (USA) Inc.

From *The Poetry of Robert Frost*, "Stopping by Woods on a Snowy Evening," published by Henry Holt, copyright 1942. Reprinted by permission.

"Not Waving But Drowning" by Stevie Smith, published by New Directions Publishing Corp. Reprinted with kind permission.

Excerpt from the work of Anaïs Nin, copyright Harcourt Education. Reprinted by permission.

Excerpt from the work of George Orwell, copyright Harcourt Education. Reprinted by permission.

Excerpt from "The Hollow Men" by T.S. Eliot, copyright Harcourt Education. Reprinted by permission.

Excerpt from *The Evolution of Jane* by Cathleen Schine. Copyright 1998 by Cathleen Schine. Reprinted by permission of Houghton Mifflin Company. All rights reserved.

Two or Three Things I Know for Sure by Dorothy Allison. Published in 1996 by Plume, a division of Penguin Group (USA) Inc. Reprinted by permission.

"Carolina in the Morning," words by Gus Kahn, copyright 1922 by Jerome H. Remick and Co.

The lines appearing at the close of Part One are attributed to Pastor Martin Niemöller and appear in slightly different wording in other sources.

Part One

For their children

FROM: Ed
Bound Matters
3330 Hatters Lane
Summitt, PA 19000

To: Scott A. Matthews
365 S. Hardwick Avenue
Summitt, PA 19000

September 8, 1998

Dear Scott,
When last you left the bookshop—fourth and fifth sets of Proust under arm—I went to return the copy of *Buddhism Without Beliefs* you'd read to its place. Before setting it down I absentmindedly flipped the book from back to front, the love stroke of any book lover, and it fell open to two quotes prefacing the text. There, to my surprise, are words of Marcel Proust. Some would call this coincidence, others the very hand of God. My preference is not to take much stock in such events, merely to take note, and my mental notes are many. The trouble is, how to retrieve them, and how to put them to good use? I leave thoughts of God to fundamentalists, who push their deities in the way a romance novel is pushed by its publisher. And I leave coincidence to the Freudians, who seem to want to take the fun out of chance encounters, theory being "there are no accidents."
I believe in a certain randomness of events. But since it's also been suggested there are only seven basic plots (leaving one scholar to conclude no new story's been told since Cervantes penned *Don Quixote*), it follows that separate lives

should give rise to like experience. This could explain what so often goes by the name *coincidence.*

We are chance encounter: an accident awaiting its happening. The heretofore evening customer on his way to one of the innumerable coffee shops that have recently sprung up in town, finding us unexpectedly open, thus becoming a morning customer. And not simply ordering, but following through on—of all things—five sets of *Remembrance of Things Past* in a single week. I discouraged you from it in spite of myself. It was as though a prophecy had come true. But I am not the prophet; I am his beneficiary.

My first experience with Proust came when I began in the book business some twenty-five years ago and wondered aloud why my employer stocked a seven-volume work by an author I'd not heard of, whose name I mispronounced, and which seemed only to be gathering dust upon the shelf. I was young, hungry, and very keen on making the rapid killing of the day.

"Proust is the standard of French literature," I was abruptly told.

I suppose I had better read him, I thought with a matching abruptness.

And I did, in a fashion, and I was immediately smitten. This was the old C.K. Scott Moncrieff translation done up in seven Vintage Books paperbacks. I still possess the souvenir of that now brittle and yellowed copy of *Swann's Way* I first read. The type is unmercifully tiny, but my eyes were younger then than yours are now—by about a decade, I would estimate, though judging from those small rectangular frames, my eyes held up better than yours. That opening page and sentence: "For a long time I used to go to bed early..." went through my heart as unswervingly as one of Cupid's arrows, and the still unhealed wound continues to influence the way I look at things. I had never read prose like that before. And I was very young, hungry in each of the ways a person can be, and I, too, suffered a broken heart. In short, I was vulnerable. Vulnerable to Proust, vulnerable to the circumstance that had brought me to Philadelphia. Had I known what I was coming to, I would never have come. But a broken romance can make a person behave stupidly, and I did. It was yet another kind of romance—the love of literature—that brought me here, but the circumstance was more like the days of arranged marriages where the wedding couple did not see one another till the bride's veil was lifted on the wedding day. Now all is lifted long before.

Romance is not dead, of course. People just discover it a bit later, after the sexual drives are satisfied. Only then does the value of foreplay become apparent. And all of this is very Proustian.

One of those seven basic plots, the Hollywood version, at least, is "boy gets girl, boy loses girl, boy gets girl back." The twist today is as likely to be "girl turns out to be boy in drag," which is all the more Proustian. But I'd rather keep these affairs at their simplest for now.

My greatest hope is that things go well with you and that your biological clock does not wind down before you have a chance to marry and build that family. But remember, too, if things do not work out exactly in that way, what Mrs. Madrigal of *Tales of the City* says: "There are all kinds of families." Reading groups, for instance. I hope you didn't blow yours by coming on too soon to Proust. But if so, remind yourself that Bound Matters opens at 7:30 a.m., and that I miss your morning visits.

Ed

P.S. *Remembrance of Things Past* is number 45 on our bestseller list dated September 8, 1998. Thank you.

FROM: Ed
Bound Matters
3330 Hatters Lane
Summitt, PA 19000

To: Dr. George Hallowell
42 Ramstead Place
Middle-of-the-Road, PA 19000

March 1, 1999

Dear Dr. Hallowell,

You may recall our brief meeting outside Devon Hall at the conclusion of the Fontanne Lecture Series earlier this winter. We were introduced by Betsy Eckerd, mutual friend and long-time colleague of yours. She suggested the three of us might share in a late supper at a favorite restaurant. I declined. Always the good Samaritan, Betsy had managed to coax me from my hibernation that evening, but frankly the lecture had edged me back toward sleep. A heavy meal would've likely turned me into even less of a conversationalist.

"Another time, then," Betsy concluded.

I am taking advantage of that tentative introduction to contact you now, not for want of psychiatric treatment, but for the smaller comforts of a professional's opinion. You may contend my question would be better put to a counselor or clergyman, that I needlessly—indeed foolishly—brought down a problem on myself. A person of greater maturity would have curbed his passion, not paused to rubberneck at the scene of the accident. I've considered and reconsidered these. Always I'm reminded of Rosa Parks in her refusal to give up a seat. Did she do the right thing by breaking a rule? As I recall, tradition has it she wasn't making a moral or even a political statement, but suffered from a bad spell of tired feet. History happened to follow. The tired feet detail is like many in stories so frequently told they take on the quality of myth. It is the debunking of myth that concerns me here. What I ask, Dr. Hallowell, is that you empty your mind of its customary lore and hear my story out.

But let me begin more properly at the beginning.

During the spring of 1997, I lent my dear friend Nancy several recordings of the Native American folksinger Buffy Sainte-Marie, my hunch being Nancy would enjoy them. When she failed to be moved by the force and tremor so distinctive to Buffy, I began composing a group of letters with the cumbersome title "On Not Being Able to Feel the Words of Buffy Sainte-Marie." They quickly became my Sunday morning meditations, the equivalent of another person's church attendance or prayer, one letter written per week and sent along to Nancy.

Then, as now, I lived on the uppermost floor of an apartment building in Philadelphia, a onetime wine distillery reincarnated as living quarters. I call it my house of spirits. For many years, I shared this two-bedroom with Patrick, another dear though troubled friend. He could have used your help, but for complex reasons I intend to make clear, would never have sought it.

On May 12th that same spring, Patrick took his life by leaping from the fire escape landing of our house of spirits. The death certificate records that he fell at 5:20 p.m., and was dead at 5:25. Since no one witnessed the fall, I'm left guessing how such calculations are made, and can only hope he spent those last minutes entirely unconscious.

It was this private wedding of fragile body to hard pavement that killed him, but there's a world outside, large and invasive, that slowly pushed him to that end. Six years previous, Patrick was diagnosed manic-depressive. A chain-smoking alcoholic, he died out of work and in debt, was HIV-positive, and had been openly homosexual for all his adult life. Once gregarious and upbeat, the kind of person who kindled parties by making people laugh, he loved theatre, female vocalists, and reading books about the English monarchy, movie stars, and the Jewish Holocaust. A more manic taste you can hardly imagine. But while his public persona may have sparkled with wit, he was privately quiet, even sullen, so that I've come to regard his symptoms like a line of toppling dominoes, the final tip exceeding the edge.

We were never romantically involved, but as close friends shared expenses and many interests for nearly twenty years. Or so it went until the enormity of Patrick's problems overtook all other interests, leaving him alone with his addictions—the man an island none of us is said to be. Our love most often went unspoken, as love in friendship frequently does, its expression left waiting within when finally it is too late.

The day before the suicide I wrote Nancy one of my Sunday morning meditations, this dealing largely with Patrick's decline. With the suicide, those letters stopped. I wept openly at the funeral (the ritual seems made for it), then slipped quietly into mourning. My concentration gone, simple tasks went undone, while the larger ones loomed like mountains.

That cool spring gave in to a warm summer. The summer passed. The year-end holidays came, then went, their new year in tow. Spring and summer again repeated their labored routine. I began to think of myself as the intermittent cicada, whose loud, arcing song returns every seven years. I resigned myself to the wait.

Like Patrick, I maintain my share of problems. Unlike him, I've learned better means of keeping them at bay. I can drink socially without reaching drunkenness, don't suffer a depressive disorder, am neither HIV-positive nor in debt—remain, in fact, gainfully employed.

But I, too, am homosexual. Gay, as they say. I came out around my twentieth year, and given the times, the transition might have been tougher. This was the early seventies, so I could look back upon the more conventional fifties while riding luckily on waves of the burgeoning gay movement. I adjusted to my perversity, made friends, had affairs, fell in love. Today I hear it called a lifestyle, but I prefer to think of it more simply as life as it has always been, and that the larger movement is only as good as the fulfillment of the solitary player. I turn forty-seven this year.

Estimates vary, of course. Some say we are one in ten, some say one in twenty. Others knock the figure down to a more comfortable two or three per hundred. An accurate reading will be impossible to obtain so long as stigmas remain—and they certainly do. Whatever the count, it's obvious we are a minority in the truest sense, the ratio of gay to straight males hovering somewhere in that one in ten-to-twenty vicinity. Given this Jonah's fish of a difference, you'd think it strange that in the twenty-odd years since I stepped out of that notorious closet, I've not once found myself overtly attracted to a straight man. But that's the way it is, as if by opening one door a second had been closed, locked shut.

Now if Patrick had been sunshine in my life, he'd been clouded over for a good while, his climax a total eclipse. It was there in darkness my dreams were shaped, nightly told tales employing a large cast, yet always dominated by Patrick. I've never held with those who go for literal symbols in dreams, insisting water must indicate a sexual theme, for example, not taking into account you may have drunk too much wine the night before and have a thirst. But while I doubt the Rosetta stone will be found to crack their code, dreams do talk to us, if only by proxy, often announcing the thing we least want to hear.

One night I was pulled from a sound sleep and sprang to my feet because I heard Patrick crying for help. Even when I was fully awake, the cry stayed with me like a voice among many jangling in the head of a madman. When it refused to clear, I accepted my insomniac's fate, walked to the living room, and put on some mindless television.

Not all my dreams were so cloyingly terrible as that. I'm in mind of the little black comedy where a former friend—one who'd left the scene because of Patrick's erratic behavior—reappeared at our apartment door with an enormous pizza box held above his head.

"What's that?" I asked, astonished by the sheer size of it.

"Oh," the answer came in the dismissive tone of a waiter at a posh restaurant. "That's Patrick. Had to make a few cuts to get him to fit."

I woke with a start. Given the high cost and low nature of coffins, here was a viable alternative, but I failed at first light to sense either the dream's humor or its lesson in economy.

My dreams gradually took on a more complacent content and subsided, only to return when I met Scott.

Just how Scott jimmied the door separating me from the heterosexual male is a mystery best left to wiser men. Yet I was there, bore witness to my own seduction, and will testify it rivals any other. Were the formula accountable, like recipes for Coke or Kentucky Fried, I'd patent it and make my fortune. But some things can't be had for pocket change. I don't carry a photo of Scott, and won't bother to describe his looks. A-minus, B-plus category, yes, but falling short of those models in fashion ads who are there to sell clothing, yet haven't a stitch on. I don't mean to discount beauty's role, only to suggest that if looks were the responsible party in this unlikely affair, what prevented its happening a hundred times before?

The answer belongs to the story ahead.

Dreams of Patrick returned with Scott, so now my nights are haunted by two alternating hosts. It could be I am permanently stuck with their leitmotif, the baddest spell of tired feet I've known. But pain isn't only the voice of a nag. It's also a reminder of something gone wrong needing repair.

The "Dear Scott" letter beginning "When last you left the bookshop..." was my initial attempt to inform its recipient the author's feelings ran deeper than first supposed. I believe most any woman reading it will recognize the gentle love letter I intended. Scott, however, did not, leading me back to a once-familiar place I thought I'd left behind. For our friendship to remain genuine, to grow, I needed to figure a means of being more explicit.

So I devised my scheme.

Remembering the letters I'd called "On Not Being Able to Feel the Words of Buffy Sainte-Marie," I resumed their production, beginning at the very spot they'd left off, with Patrick's demise. But while this second start was written as though to Nancy, they were mailed instead to Scott, turning him into an involuntary voyeur and repeat witness to my own seduction. I picked a new title, and on the outside of each envelope wrote

ENCLOSED:
HOW SCOTT AARON MATTHEWS
CAN CHANGE YOUR LIFE

followed by a number indicating sequence. That way Scott would know he was on a continuum and could exercise that particularly masculine need for always being in control. However improbable, he stayed the course, the result being that I am now in possession of copies of those same letters.

This brings me, Dr. Hallowell, back to where I began.

My initial thought was to ask if you feel it proper for a gay man to express affection for a straight man, the question precluding any sexual act. The reference is to informing only, the assumption being that sexuality isn't simply about the means to orgasm. Allowing this premise, what is left but the finesse of delivery? My revised question then is this: are rules of human intercourse themselves proper when they smell of exclusivity and a double standard?

I am directing this to you since our mutual friend Betsy tells me your clientele consists largely of gay men and lesbians, and that with them you've had continuing success. While they lack a legal footing, same-sex relations do share in every other aspect of their opposite-sex counterparts. And no document, no therapy yet exists that smoothes the course of true love. How, then, do you remedy a troubled gay man, knowing his problems aren't inherent, but are instead a response to the attitudes of others? His marginal status and faulty self-worth do not stem from confusion, paranoia, or mental disorder. They go on being written into law and are exalted from the highest pulpits, as though that law were God's own.

I recall that when I came out, one rallying cry easing passage was self-acceptance, basic stuff the heterosexual majority takes for granted. But with regard to this minority, it may succeed only in becoming another form of camouflage—a keep-it-to-yourself acceptance. Unlike ethnicity, sexual orientation is a largely invisible condition requiring some activity to become evident. And if Rosa Parks had settled for self-acceptance alone, she might still be without a seat.

Though my interest in your appraisal is genuine, Dr. Hallowell, neither affirmations nor denials can influence my association with Scott. That is a done deal, and while I see the way ahead as both long and tricky, I proceed as if this story were fixed and gone to press. By ignoring those prophets born of exclusivity, I crafted the eleven letters before you. I wish no more than that you consider their content.

Sincerely,
Ed

How Scott Aaron Matthews Can Change Your Life

A Meditation, Written as a Letter to Nancy Stuart

Life deceives us so much that we come to believing that literature has no relation with it and we are astonished to observe that the wonderful ideas books have presented to us are gratuitously exhibited in everyday life, without risk of being spoilt by the writer.

—Marcel Proust, *Time Regained*

September 16, 1998

Dear Nancy,

You may wonder why you've not heard a word from me concerning Patrick's suicide. If ever there was a thing that called for airing in my life, surely it is this. I did attempt to continue "On Not Being Able to Feel the Words of Buffy Sainte-Marie," sketched a few uneven pages, then put it aside. That oddly down-turned thought meeting up with details of the suicide brought me so low I felt if I persisted, my heart would simply stop. Time was in need of passing. So I stuck to the skeleton of my old routine, going to the bookshop each day, doing nothing to aggravate emotion. I cleaned the apartment, caught up on unread *New Yorker*s, napped frequently, and reminded myself when it was mealtime. For now my meals are most often taken alone.

By my count the passage of time amounts to one year, four months, four days, and some hours. Likely this deadened tenure would have gone on longer, closer to two full years, before the weight of mourning began its shedding, like clumps of a dog's winter coat in summer. But circumstance has nudged me to the moment at hand, and for this I am grateful. Clock and heartbeat are again in sync.

Among the things Patrick left behind was a premature suicide note written more than three years before the actual event. From the date of its composition his life became a pipeline to that end, a notice that the show was about to fold. In the note he made no mention of his alcoholism, the diagnosis of manic-depression, or the fact of his HIV-positive status. All of these he put under the tent of a simple, self-imposed generic label: "I am a mess." This is the big top, arguably the greatest show on earth, with seating arrangements for us all. To Patrick's credit, he did not take up the tiresomely common stand of blaming his parents for his predicament. On the contrary. In this regard he spoke only of love, citing both Mom and Dad as the best parents anyone could hope to have had. Sad to say, he did mention the church, and it was only to the church that he pointed specific blame. Patrick wrote:

> I remember myself as a boy—I was so religious and I loved the church and the Blessed Mother so much—and they shit in my face. "You're gay so go die!" It was devastating for me to think the church I loved so well could do this.

I cannot read these words without feeling Patrick's pain cut through me almost as though we shared the same flesh. And even though the two of you never met, I imagine you can feel it, too. Here is an unrequited love that could not be quenched by even a thousand sexual unions. Given the sum of Patrick's problems, I find it notable that he should single out the church with its sting of homophobia. That self-loathing placed so early in Patrick's life was a real time bomb tick, tick, ticking, and his note is tangible evidence of how destructive homophobia can be. All the other negatives in Patrick's life followed in due course as if to fulfill the requirements of what it is to be homosexual, the final act being that he should leap to his death. I would never have given voice to this thought while he lived. To so much as think that thought too loudly might have mysteriously increased the likelihood.

Sex is no ordinary delight like the ingestion of a chocolate. Its place and hold stand very nearly outside evolutionary practice, though they would be meaningless without it—like this thought without its thinker, or the sound of my one hand jacking. The thwarting of sexual desire would bring a quick end to the species, but that is not to say its sole purpose is to bring forth children. If this were so, love and its rituals would be confined to that single heterosexual gesture bound by the parameters of the childbearing years. Who knows the iniquity of this narrow interpretation better than any gay person who has loved? And who that has taken a breath has not at least once loved? From childhood sweetheart, to best buddy, to marriage, love is our primary adhesive.

Yet look all around us at the confusion, especially in regard to sex—just how mixed the messages are. Sex exists everywhere on the one hand, and is as often the no-no of the wagging finger on the other. It carries the main characters of almost any theatre piece you can think of, and is the subliminal message in every lesser story, from the cigarette ad to the polish on your teeth and the brazen red of your lipstick. And the twelve-year-old child who is left alone to wonder about it all turns into the adult who knows only how to giggle at its mention, then proceeds to dim the lights on the next generation. On the subject of sex, we refuse to grow up.

Patrick, I remember, had a stash of male-on-male pornography in his bedroom—several magazines and a few videos. Not long before he died, he destroyed these. I can attest to this because I looked for them—very hard. This is meant to make you smile, but it is also meant to make you sense the sadness in his need to obliterate that part of himself. It is as though this was the great crime of his life, a thing to be hidden, even in death.

Patrick, I believe, did not mean for his suicide note to survive. It was written straight out as a letter to his parents on yellow sheets borrowed from me one desperate evening. The words are jagged and smudged with tears or the spill of his drink. Most people would have trouble deciphering them.

On another evening several weeks after the note had been written, I found myself drawn to the open door of Patrick's bedroom. It was the dinner hour and Patrick had succumbed to his nightly ritual, had blacked out, and slept quietly in his favorite chair. Passing beneath the arch of the bedroom door, I saw that the note had found its way to the bottom of a pile of papers on Patrick's bureau. The sunny yellow of my legal-pad stationery stood out. I pulled it from its place and read it for the first time. Sensing the note would never be mailed, I then squirreled it away in my own bedroom, not to find and read it again until the summer after Patrick's death. Surely this violated his privacy, but I justified my little theft because the yellow sheets had been a loan. I was simply taking back what belonged to me, words and all. Now I see the importance of this sad, easily overlooked document. There may be thousands like it lost to other piles in other rooms. Or a million more no one ever bothered to write.

It is today, with a third reading, that I see my way to take up work begun by others, and clarify the words.

The topic dominating the news this entire summer has been a Presidential sex scandal. You know the one and all the names that have gone down with it. There's hardly a niche left on the nightly broadcasts for the Dow Jones or Nasdaq averages, sex being about the only topic capable of displacing our interest in the monetary. Has our President behaved wisely? Hardly. Has he always been honest? Diogenes yet wanders. Has he used the Oval Office in ways other than intended? I guess. Has there ever been a President more human? I would say not. Might you or I do the same, given the position, the power, the right person, wrong time? I wish here only to speak for myself—but I think so. How quickly has the rush to judgment come from persons harboring no fewer sexual thoughts than he? Very quickly. How swiftly would Jesus have run to his side, perhaps even arm-in-arm with a woman of low repute, as if to say, "I am as you are and you are as I am"? Swiftly indeed.

Somewhere in *Remembrance of Things Past*, Marcel Proust wrote that we become moral only after we become unhappy. In our President's case it might be said that he has begun becoming moral only after having been caught. And pity the poor man who is so unlucky as to never be caught and miss out on the redemptive power of having to ask forgiveness. Happiness and unhappiness are not options in life but are the unavoidable consequences of having lived. And where the one happens, the other follows. As wise men tell us, the middle way is best, but they know best of all that no one has ever found that middle passage who did not once find himself in the ditch.

Curious, but I cannot figure out in this summer of scandal whether I have just fallen into a ditch—or out of one. It would seem that I have been oddly blessed with the stirrings of love, and that these feelings could easily be judged "inappropriate." But I would say whenever love is genuine, it cannot be said to be anything except appropriate, however troublesome. So what tag should I affix to these stirrings? Sexual? Lustful? Genuinely loveful? I have spun the casino's wheel again and again, but this woebegone marble is refused a place. I will say that one moment I am filled with delicious rapture, the next that I am squirming in discomfort—and that our President's example sheds no light on my conflict. So I must pose the question: could anyone who would slice a fruit down the middle say, as he watches the two halves fall in opposite directions, that one half contains the love, the other half the lust? I wonder in such a compartmentalization of affections whether that person has ever experienced either the love or the lust? Or does he go through life always dropping the one in favor of the other, then the other in favor of the one, only to end by dismissing the snarl and retreating to the easier sum of his bank balance?

In the ditch or out? In the Oval Office or the Blue Room?—or possibly riding up in an elevator? In lust or love? Why is it I cannot pick up even the tiniest stone and hurl it? It is because I knew a man called Patrick who threw himself from a building because of whom he happened to love. And not in response to any specific love lost, but only from the tugs of a vague, a haunting preference, whose practice infringes on no one. Whichever way our President falls, however his office, marriage, and family are punctured, he will not fall with a gesture half so hollow as that.

I must be off now to the drudgery of the day and to bookselling, but the lurid details of the Ed scandal will quickly follow.

For a brief spell I hope to push out of your mind that other affair so meticulously retold at taxpayers' expense in The Starr Report. On these yellow sheets, like Patrick in his suicide note before me, I will willingly, yes, willfully write my own sun, moon, and star report—and live. And though this tale will not wend its way to the forefront of the evening news, the news may be the poorer for it. You might even come to call it memorable.

Ed

September 17, 1998

Dear Nancy,

On Saturday, August fifteenth, while I was out of the shop retrieving a sandwich for lunch, a customer placed a book order with my long-standing business partner, Al.

The following Monday morning my routine went largely unaltered. Arriving at the shop, I undid *The New York Times* from its wrapper, snapped on lights and the radio (which played a familiar bit of Sibelius), then gathered the weekend orders. One index card among them seemed to stand out, and I paused at the title: *On Love*, by Alain de Botton. I hesitated again when I saw the customer was Scott Matthews, the name so familiar it greeted me with a convivial *hello*. Nothing odd there. Memory plays tricks, and likely this was neither the first nor last Scott Matthews I'd encounter among that parade of characters coming to Bound Matters in search of a book. Given how common some surnames are, you'd think those in charge of the flexible dubbing would await an inspired moment. But no, the result a tiresome bumper crop of Bills and Bobs, Jacks and Joes. That is, until the next upstart aligns himself with celebrity status. Then the marquees will be weighted in another direction, with Brookes and Dianas, or variations on Elisabeth and Elysia. There is a measure of comfort, I suppose, in all this similitude: being different is one thing, being noticeably different yet another. So it's in the odds that what washes up on shore is the likes of Scott Matthews. Seeing the footprint in the sand, its shape like an old friend turned up in time, I was still unable to make a mental match of print to face. But I stole a third moment and jotted down both name and phone number and put them at the back of my box of orders, the place where I keep names I refer to often.

"I know Scott, though Scott I'm not." The weak rhyme drifted through my head as if the ears were opposite doors opening onto an empty room. Isn't that something out of Dr. Seuss, or have I only confused this with the familiar lines from *Green Eggs and Ham*?

I then phoned our supplier and placed our daily order, which included Scott's request. *On Love* arrived punctually the following morning. In a kind of go-to-the-head-of-the-class maneuver, I left the rest of the order sitting neglected in its box, snapped up Scott's book and phoned him at once. The Supremes may insist that love can't be hurried, but I have yet another theory, that it is easily overlooked by those not paying attention. Scott's taped voice, sunny and clear, clicked on his machine. "Hi!" the message began. "This is Scott...." To such a pleasant sound it was easy to treat the person I thought I already knew as though he were among the shop's oldest and best customers, and I replied:

"Hi, Scott! This is Ed at Bound Matters. We have another book for you—and thanks for relying on us, as always."

On the morning of the nineteenth a young man in darkened glasses arrived at the shop shortly after I unlocked the door. "Hi," he said, an exuberant echo of his own taped message. "I had no idea you opened so early. You must be Ed." The man put out his hand to shake mine. I hesitated. "I'm Scott Matthews," the man said, his voice a prod to remind me of the dual nature of the deal. "You have a book for me." Recalling both ritual and transaction, I stuck out my arm and put my hand into his, squeezed it lightly and released it. I then turned round and fetched the copy of *On Love* from the reserve shelf.

"Got that in a hurry," Scott said.

Reconsidering my position, I thought to side with the Supremes and remind Scott that love could not be hurried, but kept my giddiness to myself, opting for the more genuine, pragmatic reason. "Can't afford to waste time," I said. "A lot of major competition out there."

"Must be tough." Scott took off his dark glasses, and in a tiny ritual I imagined had been rehearsed and performed before, replaced them with a pair of small, rectangular frames. I looked into his now clear, bespectacled eyes. Without touching, a place had been touched. "Must be tough," I seemed to hear the words repeat. "What with the encroachment of the chains and all...."

I was immediately caught in the steel-blue trap of Scott's eyes. Disarmingly deep, they seemed to refresh the cliché that eyes are, in fact, windows to the soul. Here was a place with almond-shaped borders where I could get lost in the dark wood of lashes, could linger, grow old there, and never mind the passage. My other instinct may have been to push him away, but having seen down that endless corridor, this was probably already impossible. Like Yossarian at the opening of *Catch-22*, I was instantly smitten.

But I came quickly to what was left of my senses and said, "I thought the book you ordered was one of those silly self-help books about love, but I see it's a novel."

"Probably a silly novel about love," Scott grinned. The smile momentarily distracted me from his eyes, though the double row of small white teeth placed so evenly between the full lips proved as disarming. "You mean to say you haven't read it?" Scott asked. "There's a rumor circulating that you guys have read every book."

The impossibility of that task ranks with Sisyphus trying to get the rock to stay put atop that pointed hill only to see it roll down again, and I hoped that Scott was not so shallow as to have bought in on it.

"I guess I missed this one," I said. "On principle, I avoid books with the word love in the title." It was the smallest of white lies. Were Scott a mind reader, this response might help to derail his telepathy. My darting glance returned to his eyes, then dropped, like a pinball en route, to the white shirt he was wearing. It billowed with a stylish flair and was impeccably pressed, the crisp lines on the sleeves so fine they might have been painted there by a narrow brush. Can't remember when I bothered to press a shirt like that, I was thinking. Too many more important things to do. And not a coffee stain to be seen. Probably has it done out.

"One of the fellows at the printshop where I work remembers you from when the bookshop used to be in Waynewood. Says he loved stopping by on his lunch hours and getting your recommendations." Scott described his co-worker. "Do you remember him?"

"From that description you'd think I would," I answered, but failed to. It was a successful triple play: the eyes, the smile, the shirt had all conspired to blot out my memory banks.

"He has a wickedly cynical sense of humor," Scott added in further hope of stirring my memory.

"We're very popular with cynics," I said. "Fallen Catholics and the like."

Scott laughed. Seeing what I took to be a bolt of recognition in his eyes, I asked, "You're not a fallen Catholic?"

"Not yet," Scott answered, and now our laughter chimed in unison like a pair of steeple bells.

Once again Scott cheerfully put out his hand to shake mine as he left the shop that morning. I did not hesitate this second time. Our two hands locked in anatomical correctness, the arms suspended for the moment like the cable of a great bridge, then parted.

The memory of Scott's eyes remained with me through the day, like the burned image of a sun looked at for too long. But I'd hardly looked at all. I was resistant, downright stubborn on the matter, and flatly informed myself to knock it off. Even this sounded too suggestive, and I dispensed with the fleeting thought of a liaison set among the classics. I had no time for such a tryst, not for romantic love, not even a quick sexual encounter. The icy breath of this or that corporate giant had denied me the hope of a private life lived quietly beside a stream, or more passionately under the covers.

And look what happens when Presidents give in.

Granted, as a bookseller I wasn't put into office with quite the same heady moral expectations. And though from certain angles Summit, Pennsylvania, might continue to look like a postcard town, I doubted there'd be much of a row were I discovered with a delivery man in back of the UPS truck. Might give the locals fresh fodder for the gossip mill on those chilly winter nights between horse and flower shows. What's more, like all readers, I know seduction is a frequent stop on the literary landscape. If I'd sworn anything on a Bible, it was to tell the truth of *Lolita* right alongside of Charlotte's Web—well, maybe a few shelves over. But always, whatever the material, it was with an eye for literary merit, not mere titillation. Other bookshops might turn themselves into little more than social events, thinly veiled pickup joints where books come to exist as makeshift coasters for high-strung caffeine pushers. Soon some mega-chain will be acquiring a liquor license, and then the circle will be complete. Now there's an idea to generate a billion in annual revenues and give the current big boys something to sweat about! I can hear them in their think tanks coming up with musical slogans, the cute logos soon to flash in neon and occupy fifty thousand square feet at a shopping mall near you.

But no such carryings-on at Bound Matters. Scott had come to put a book in his hand and to shake mine—nothing more. Don't even think about it.

Thinking about it or not, in the course of the August dog days that followed, Scott did actually become the shop's best customer. Having read *On Love* and finding it to his liking, Scott was primed for more, and I was primed for the priming.

In just two days Scott returned to the shop. Fresh from a morning shower, he smelled of scent, his dark hair whipped and set like a rich frosting atop a vanilla cake. With the excited look of a paperboy doing rounds to make payment on his first bicycle, he held a printout from one of the on-line bookstores. Handing it to me, Scott asked, "Do you have any of these?" I looked at the slick sheet of paper. The graphics were uninteresting, with no touch of the homespun, and they said nothing to me. Beneath a stoic portrait of the author, all of Alain de Botton's books were listed in neat alphabetical order. The guy staring out of the picture was not someone I would readily take advice from on love, but Scott had stumbled on his mentor. Skimming the capsule reviews on the page, I saw that there was not a discouraging word to be heard in what amounted to a glossy advertisement. This was from the "buy it, you'll like it" school of criticism—and I wasn't buying. But I was also forgetting my place. It was Scott who was in need of servicing.

The only one of de Botton's books Bound Matters had on hand was *How Proust Can Change Your Life*. This is one of those annoying titles that booksellers who still stock genuine bookstores don't like because it isn't clear where it should be shelved. In self-help, literary criticism, or in literature next to the original work and author himself? Or might it belong in humor? On this day I found it in criticism. Scott purchased the book and ordered a third de Botton title, *Kiss and Tell* (a common practice reaching up to the highest office in the land). Again I found myself drawn into the steel-blue duo of Scott's eyes. And yes, once more he wore a prissily pressed, dazzling white shirt, only this time the glint of a gold cuff link fastened the end of each stiff sleeve. It was far too warm for such a formality, and you'd think the inky printshop where Scott was bound would be least conducive to the wearing of white. I ventured a guess: this fellow was the last of his generation to be sexually repressed. For him, I thought, Intercourse remains a quaint Pennsylvania town stocked with plain-clothed Amish. *Cuff links*. I've never even owned a pair of cuff links. Probably has it done out.

Taking further note of the Lord Fauntleroy attire, the possible years of extended sexual denial, and the fact that every ten seconds or so someone somewhere is being picked up in one of those chain bookstores, I was seriously thinking of saying to Scott, "What lovely eyes you have!" No matter that it was eight in the morning. I could hardly be fresher, and it was actually Scott who had introduced the subject as he went on in that now animated white shirt about the insights de Botton exposed in *On Love*. Only a nudge, and he could be talking dirty. And mine was hardly a station of rigid authority, neither scoutmaster nor Episcopal priest (as if that had ever stopped anyone). Nor was Scott seventeen, but a mature thirty, maybe thirty-five. I could still pass for thirty-nine in a poor light.

If possibilities there'd been, all these shrank to Walter Mitty musings when I opened my mouth, and out came, "What a beautifully pressed shirt for such a warm and humid day." Sublimation may have its place, but what a transparent, even stupid thing for one man to be saying to another. Might he return the stroke and make an admiring remark about my hair? Could I then broach the topic of his eyes, the come-on smile, and whatever was to follow?

But before any of this had a chance to kick in, Scott winked and said, "It won't last." He then pushed the smile to its limit so that the dimples dug deep into his cheeks and became matching whirlpools tugging me in. Soon the weakening structure of my legs would need to be stamped: "This property is condemned."

As Scott left the shop that morning, the bridge of our handshake again spanned the rapidly closing chasm between us, and I found myself thinking of all the other uses those same two hands had been put to over the years—perhaps Scott was thinking the same. I could have easily taken his last-ditch opportunity and wrestled him to the floor. If Mrs. H. should arrive in her feathered hat, I could claim I was trying out some sort of fancy new aikido hold. Those feathers, I swear, sprout from her very own head—she won't know the difference. Or else I could plant a "goodnight kiss" on Scott's forehead, like that one Marcel—or is it Proust himself?—so long awaits in the Overture to *Swann's Way*. But I ended without either fancy hold or goodnight kiss, accepting instead the casual intimacy of Scott's handshake, as is. Nevertheless, it was that memorable morning, one of those moments on which sonnets turn, when Scott Aaron Matthews left the bookshop with a copy of *How Proust Can Change Your Life* under his arm.

MARCEL PROUST. Rhymes with roost, not roast, or "roust"-about. Proust is someone not often encountered in the lower levels of an average American education. He is kept tucked in the uppermost echelons with advanced students of the French language and its literature. But once a student is made aware of him, the name of Marcel Proust begins appearing everywhere.

Proust intimidates. Proust is postponed, to be put off until retirement, or that summer you find yourself laid up with a bad back. His grand work, *Remembrance of Things Past*, can be thought of as either a novel in seven parts, or seven interlocking novels. Either way, it runs to some three thousand three hundred pages in its English translation and is considered by many to be the greatest of all French novels. Or, less nationalistically, the triumph of early modernism. It's big, anyway, so that though Proust may not always change a life, he can easily dominate one.

But the reputation is not so straightforward as this notion of "great" may imply. It would not be far off the mark to say that among the French, Proust has come to be regarded as a god, and his text as the son's gospel, not to be tinkered with by any mere mortal. But it was not always so, and elsewhere still the reputation, while strong, is riddled with holes, misgivings, apologies. Perhaps, like the sex scandal currently preoccupying the nation, Proust illuminates the difference between the European and the rest of the West's mentality. It could be added that the word reputation is a cup holding both a good- and bad-girl persona.

If you break Remembrance into its seven parts, or further into thirteen, or splinter the whole into quotable morsels, its floridness may go on intimidating. Put simply: Proust is different, a world unto himself. The prose is ornate, seeming at first distinctly not modern. Some have called it purple, others pink—and this pinkish quality has not a thing to do with the threat of Communism. The descriptive details are many, and the sentences into which they are poured can reach a great length. But the sensibility of *In Search of Lost Time* is neither of 19th nor 20th century, nor of any century in particular. It is the cracked cup of Buddhist thought where distinctions between good girl and bad girl dissolve. And such a dissolution can threaten the Western mind, so bent on compartmentalization and a rush to judgment.

To read *Remembrance* requires commitment, like the raising of a child, which is in part why Proust's following includes so many gay people and the leisured ladies of another era. But for even those to whom *Remembrance* seems impenetrable, it can hold a distanced fascination, like the Rubik's Cube you can neither solve nor let alone. As does the odd, cork-lined apartment of its author, adding bric-a-brac to the legend. With Proust, the tangle of an artist's life and work is most maddeningly fused.

There are few authors, to stress the point in this brief outline, whose modified names have become part of the language. We say *Shakespearean*, we say *Dickensian*, and we say *Proustian*. A handful in all. When we say *Shakespearean*, I suppose we are referring to something of his grandiloquence. With *Dickensian*, it is the elaborate plots, the characters—sometimes goofy, often prudish—and the drafty, gray settings in a time when boys had a greater propensity to be orphaned. With *Proustian*, the reference is to time itself. Time, memory, and timelessness. Also a linking to the development of psychoanalytic thought. Freud was born fifteen years before Proust and lived seventeen years beyond Proust's death. And though these two never met, it would seem they shared more than a juncture in history, so that when we say *Freudian*, we touch upon *Proustian*.

Allow me to presume that all art strives to break from its own time, to outstep the whims of fad and fancies. In this there is both a vanity and an impracticality. An artist's creation is a child unable to endure the presence of its parent for too long. No artist, in any case, is so designed to know the full fate of his offspring. And the thing he creates cannot know, for it regains consciousness only in the eye, the ear, or—what should I say?—the soul of its next beholder. But with *A la recherche du temps perdu*, Proust makes the statement at the top. His seven-pronged work and the echoes within are a kind of stopwatch. Proust stops the clock

—here—

and sifts into a single moment a great mix of detail, grief, passing events of the day, love experienced, lost, then regained, fixed finally like initials carved in a tree's bark. Therein lies the bite. He is telling a story, but it is a story which begins at the ending and ends at the beginning—or is it the other way round? From wherever you start, *Remembrance* becomes all the more maddening if you try to impose upon it conventional expectations of how a story ought to be told. But if instead, having thought you recognized the footprint in the sand, you can free yourself from those expectations, letting go and losing yourself to it, you may slowly—so long as a baby doesn't need minding—fall in love.

Now hold it. I may have lost me. Did he say, "fall in love"? It's a bothersome task, the phrase itself a simpleminded contradiction, the great grandpapa of all oxymorons. If love is that important thing, a thing said to alter the course of a life and to which other responsibilities should give way, how is it that anyone who has ever experienced love should fall? Adam and Eve fell naked out of Eden, and that should have put an end to it—but the coverup was only begun there. The rest of us seem redundantly to take up the task, generation after generation, foppishly fussing with our fig leaves as if we'd come upon something new. In the act of this repeated fall, we swipe lamely at the air as we drop, since neither God nor Darwin (or whoever is to be held accountable) has lent us suitable wings.

But everyone in love expresses it so. At a later moment, comfortably distanced from the spot and ensconced in mediocrity, he can say, "That wasn't love, but infatuation, a drunken moment, something to be deleted from the final text so that no one can suggest how flawed a character I am. Surely *not* true love, but a passing fancy, the captivity of something as inconsequential as a pair of steel-blue eyes."

Fiddlesticks. Either the memory has been repressed, or the experience simply forgotten, sidestepped in favor of more tangible fare. But it is real. Take it away and the universe would have nowhere to go. And it remains real, and can be reawakened by an artist capable in the way of Marcel Proust. He knows that those of us left out of love are secretly jealous of those in the thick of it, even when it is at its most painful, when that inevitable ache comes that cannot be satisfied, no matter how sustained the goodnight kiss. Love lies somewhere in the Proustian desert of time touching timelessness. It simply has no use for secrets.

Ed

September 19, 1998

Dear Nancy,

When Scott next came into the shop he was fired with a curiosity about Marcel Proust. He'd read *How Proust Can Change Your Life*, and though it could not be said this transition was complete, it would seem the machinery to that end had been set in motion.

The way I saw it, the machine was already beginning to resemble some sort of Rube Goldberg contraption. You remember those. One of his machines might be called "The Stamp Affixer." The same task you and I would perform with ease by tearing the stamp from its perforated place, licking and then slapping it to an envelope, the Rube Goldberg device needlessly complicates. The stamp, wet tongue, and awaiting envelope are replaced by a cumbersome bureaucracy of levers and pulleys, balls and tunnels, chutes and ladders. Plain and simple are not enough. You need the thingamabob and the doohickey, elaborate beyond purpose, neurosis in three dimensions. And if a ball goes astray, a single lever misfires, or one string doesn't pull its own weight—Kaboom!—and there's an end to it. You must then go back to the beginning, and this time with a small legion of king's horses and men there to put the contraption together again.

So imagine me applying stamp and envelope to opposite ends of this budding Rube Goldberg. My hope is for an autumn wedding, but I have developed a stammer and been assigned a room in Purgatory where the story I begin goes no further than "once upon a time," then repeats. In the midst of this dalliance, Scott busts down the door and begins to interrogate me on the topic of *Remembrance of Things Past*, as if I were its expert. My gut response may have been to put out a vertical, flattened palm and invoke the inveterate Supremes command. Instead, I am easily swayed into position, a queen ascending the throne. But not so fast, great Scott, this is no elderly or even Ellery Queen, but Proust, and my ascendancy was questionable at best.

The first time I'd cracked *Swann's Way*, I was not yet twenty-five, and some reigning monarch of that day warned me that I should not attempt to read Proust until I had passed my fortieth year. Here was that hard rock and high place where Sisyphus couldn't make it stay put. I'd already been told by one authority that Proust was the standard of French literature, as if all worthy story lines were of that one lineage, the rest a mere French leave. This was reason enough for my revolutionary spirit not to read him. But I'd been challenged. Now I was being told that I'd have to wait yet another fifteen years before I should even think of poking my head above the surface of that standard. And what can someone over forty tell someone not yet twenty-five that he doesn't already know? The short cut to Granny's house must be here somewhere, I thought, and if I don't begin looking for it, I just might be stewing porridge well into middle age. So forget the parlor chores, Cinderella, I informed myself: I will read that Handsome Prince Proust. It will be like getting drunk at sixteen, copping a feel—or possibly even going all the way, the partner of one's dreams an exotic mix of beauty and oversized genitalia. Little did I know how much of all that there is to be found in Proust, that there could be something to those rumors about Frenchmen that goes beyond the chocolate pudding accent. Even less did I suspect how every affair in Proust goes wrong, that *In Search of Lost Time* may be the greatest Rube Goldberg of all time, and that the only thing in it that gets laid down right is the writing of the book itself.

But for all the hyperbole and instruction manuals, the getting laid part is not the challenging feature of romantic scheming. Sex is a dependable commodity purchasable on any street corner—at the newsstand if not in the flesh. Love is the quixotic thing. Whereas sex leads to a climax and a nap, love is a sinkhole never satisfied, the already-described fall without a net.

And what confronted me at this moment was no Frenchman, but one Scott Aaron Matthews. The name suggests a stubborn blend of Old and New Testaments with a WASPish update, thumb-indexed for quick reference and bound in expensive leather, nothing kinky. Whether getting laid, falling in love, or discovering a fancy hybrid betwixt the two, it was apparent I ought to be working a different street corner. Scott struck me as being about as middle of the road as a Siddhartha in post-ascetic, pre-enlightenment phase. I doubt he would be persuaded to take a little roll in the ditch: he might muss up his hair or dirty that clean white shirt.

So before Scott had a chance to notice that my crown had slipped several monarchies before, I discouraged him from taking a deep interest in Proust.

"Read the Overture from *Swann's Way*," I suggested. "If you like it, go on."

But Scott was building up steam and wouldn't hear of it. Having discovered a web site collecting some two hundred-odd thoughts from *Remembrance*, now he was smitten. Might as well swap *Anna Karenina* for *Bartlett's Familiar Quotations*, I grumbled to myself. Not much of a plot in the latter, but there's something resembling an orgasm on nearly every page. Then turning the argument on my determined Scott, I said, "Sucking up a string of quotes is not the same as approaching the text. Proust is dense, grindingly slow. Many think of him as a colossal bore drunk on his own words. Taste him, read the bit about the madeleines, but don't commit yet." I was about to say that I didn't believe a bride should go to her altar a virgin, that she ought to know something of what she's getting into. But I thought better of it and kept my own overtures in the wings.

Scott, however, was not to be talked out of his infatuation. Refusing to begin with *Swann's Way*, he instead ordered the complete boxed set of seven novels. And wanting to give Scott whatever Scott wanted, I complied. Thus for a sixty-four-dollar fee, plus tax, my young patron was about to enter a whole other world.

But it was at this threshold that Scott went too far. He told me that he was trying to put together a reading group among his friends and that the inaugural book of his choice was *Remembrance of Things Past*. Such a maiden voyage, I sensed, was doomed at the start, so that now it was my turn

—whoooa!—

to stop the clock. It is one thing that a solitary lemming should make a wrong turn, quite another when he has acquired a following.

There is a great irony in all this discouragement, and an even greater bittersweetness. Had Scott asked me what I thought of the latest John Grisham, I could have shrugged my shoulders and slipped quietly out of love. No one would have been the wiser. But fate can be a trickster of uncanny insight, and I have never known him to act with greater prowess than on this occasion. It was not so much Scott and his gathering of lemmings that were making a wrong turn, but their bookseller.

Instinct informed me that Scott was not gay, or if he were, would not be especially interested in me. Yet here was an attractive man in his thirties who appeared to live alone and who seemed, for my benefit, to be lingering longer each day in the shop. He was a bit of a clothes horse, a stickler in general when it came to appearances. He'd not said one word about football, baseball, or the kind of car he drove. The most aggressive move I'd witnessed was to his next book selection—a contact sport leading directly to Proust. And Scott wasn't waiting until the clock struck forty. The sixty-four-dollar fare wasn't hush money, but fairly screamed *this fellow might be gay*, with the jewel that twinkled at the crown's center being the total absence of a female companion. Nary a mention of a weekend date, pretty fräulein, or sweetheart.

But to what plot level had I descended? It wasn't as though I'd been ranting about a boyfriend either. My friendship with Scott had only just begun, its whisper faint as green on a tree in early spring, and his sexual orientation was of no more consequence,

I hoped, than mine would prove to him. And I don't go about choosing my friends because of what they *happen* to be, but rather for what they make of themselves. So what that I am having a little whoopee on the sly, gazing into those steel-blue eyes? No harm. Who is immune to the occasional ogle? Certainly not Scott himself. He doesn't dress up on a warm day in hope of attracting flies. And unlike our President, I do know when it is best to keep my pants up.

Pants up, perhaps, but my emotional guard was rapidly coming down. I felt as helpless as HAL being steadily unplugged. Blame that great go-between, Proust. There was no way Scott could have known the particulars of my libidinal centers and what he might be fondling.

There is an old question: if you were to be marooned on a desert isle and could take only one book with you, what would it be? My stock answer is *In Search of Lost Time*, though I always feel I'm being a little greedy, since the answer really gets you seven for the price of one. Difficult as Proust can be, he is very close to my heart and several other erogenous zones as well. There is simply so much there: obsessive heterosexual love, tea and madeleines, the Dreyfus trial, a falling aristocracy, lilting music and Impressionist painting, gay brothels—what more can anyone ask for? And unlike so many novels (is it really a novel at all?), it's a complete circle, a sort of guided tour of a whole life, or a finely detailed description of what it is to experience being alive.

In what is surely its most famous passage, Marcel puts the lip of a cup to his own and drinks:

> No sooner had the warm liquid mixed with the crumbs touched my palate than a shudder ran through me and I stopped, intent upon the extraordinary thing that was happening to me. An exquisite pleasure had invaded my senses, something isolated, detached, with no suggestion of its origin. And at once the vicissitudes of life had become indifferent to me, its disasters innocuous, its brevity

illusory—this new sensation having had on me the effect which love has of filling me with a precious essence; or rather this essence was not in me, it was me.

For me, the meaning of independent bookselling comes in leading people to such places. But in doing so, I do not impose my meanings, nor can I really lead. I can only point. And I do not point to Proust until I think a person is ready. How could I know if this newcomer Scott, hell-bent on love, so fresh and apparently intact, might be ready? Was it my place rudely to point when it seemed that Scott was seducing me behind his very own back? Or might he, like a child unable to contend with another day's wait to Christmas, have already sneaked a peek and seen that one of the later volumes of *Remembrance* is called *Sodom and Gomorrah*?—though in some translations it is camouflaged as *Cities of the Plain*. What did he think that was all about? Minneapolis/St. Paul? Perhaps before taking on Proust, I should have pointed Scott's reading group to the Old Testament. It *is* shorter.

During the next few days, Scott phoned the shop repeatedly to order additional sets of *Remembrance of Things Past*: sixty-four, one hundred twenty-eight, one hundred ninety-two dollars. The ante steadily rose with each addendum to his burgeoning reading group. And happily I often found Scott retrieving his orders at my doorstep in the mornings. All I could think was that there's a whole tribe of people out there equally smitten by those steel-blue eyes, their joint subscriptions smelling of a damned orgy in the making—and just where do I go to apply?

Scott had quickly become the most important part of my morning routine, not merely as a purchasing customer, but supplying the coffee as well. I half expected him to appear with a silver tray decked in a fussy lace cloth, lavender bouquet, tea and Tastykakes. He even went so far as to offer a hand to help keep the business going. Scott managed the Mister Quickie Printshop in Wanahavamaker, a town only a few miles up the pike. Here was a perfect marriage, his offer being to do up a single-page calendar with a Bound Matters' logo. His company would provide the graphics gratis, and we could distribute the calendars to our customers, a daily reminder in the course of the year that there is still an independent bookseller out there.

I thought of my employer and his general distrust of printers, the claim being that he'd never known one to have gotten a job done right. Surely he would think Scott had something up one of those well-pressed white sleeves. And I recalled my employer's admonishment: "Don't believe anyone who says he's not in it for the money."

"But Scott is reading Proust," I would remind him. "You remember? That standard of French literature."

The warm day came when Scott was to pick up the final sets of *Remembrance of Things Past*. His reading group was to meet for the first time that evening, a Friday. As late summer shifted to autumn, our morning routine would probably wind to a close. The de Botton titles had been quickly dispensed, each gone the route of a one-night stand. Now Scott and his companions in Proust were about to set sail on a sea of words. Some, I guessed, would founder. One or two might make the crossing, and Scott would likely be among the latter. The hour of sweet sorrows at hand, I was feeling wistful, even sad. That is the trouble with Proust: it is difficult to read him and to go on having a life of your own. Like the odd man out in a love triangle, it could be I was about to lose Scott to the very same beauty I had first loved.

I got out a copy of *Buddhism Without Beliefs*, marked three favorite pages "On Emptiness," and put it at the counter so that I would not forget to show them to Scott. He'd been so punctual the other mornings that I became suddenly unnerved when I noticed the clock: *Scott was half an hour late*. Perhaps he'd dumped me for a less pedantic scribe and a bookseller with more pronounced jugs. With equal suddenness I grew angry at myself and began to shout aloud: "This isn't a date, but a business, and it's not my habit to confuse public and private lives.

Scott is just another customer who probably makes a pit stop at the chains whenever it's convenient. I'm acting like he's family—or worse, like I'm a schoolgirl suffering a schoolgirl's crush!"

I grabbed the copy of *Buddhism Without Beliefs*, slammed it back into its place, then headed up the center aisle of the shop toward the front door.

There, as though reversed, the thunder of my fury seemed to produce the flash of Scott's dashing silhouette.

"You're late!" I said, turning the anger I'd directed at myself toward him.

Scott laughed, and hearing his delight spill into the room, I laughed, too, the steeple bells again chiming in unison. "On Fridays," Scott said, timidity creeping into his voice, "I stop for a large breakfast. Eggs and scrapple at the Farmers' Market. Or an omelet at Joe's. The guy there makes a great omelet."

"Sounds good," I said, envisioning a shared breakfast on another distant Friday. "Really good. I'm usually nibbling on yesterday's cheese purchased at the gourmet shop across the street...." I, too, was feeling timid, afraid. I hadn't planned on it, but I wanted to figure out some quick way of telling Scott what I was feeling without losing either a customer or a friend—*but how could I put it?* A shopful of words, but where were the right words for this occasion? Certainly not with the sex manuals, nor with the self-help guides and their convoluted titles, such as *I Don't Love Myself, So Why Should I Give a Drip About You?* They weren't with gender studies either, nor among the chiseled chests and torn bodices of the romance novels. Oddly enough, even the largely neglected shelf of gay studies remained mute to my questions. The words were nowhere, a missing link, and anyone I might think to ask would only suggest that I shut up about it. I could rattle out the news like that guy who talks at the speed of sound in those television commercials. The blur of words then would be like the camouflage of *Cities of the Plain*. But what would be the use of that? The problem was in the camouflage; the problem has always been the camouflage.

So instead I went on chatting happily about the sin of French cheeses to be had across the street with Jack and Barb. What I was attempting to do was to hang onto the remaining moments. As everyone does. As no one can. They belong to that river's water you pass through but once.

I went to ring up the sale of the two sets of Proust in slow motion, Scott following my lead, our gazes joined.

"Five sets of Proust in a single week!" I blurted, pumping joy into the deal as if this were something on the level of Donald Trump. "I can honestly put *Remembrance of Things Past* on our bestseller list next week, granted it will be very near the bottom." I pointed to my handwritten list of books at the counter, a semi-detached Buddha suggesting the way.

Responding to my cue, Scott took his bespectacled eyes from mine and looked directly into the heart of the list. A shudder ran through him. His glimpse swerved, returning to me, ache filling the glance the way a barrel entraps rainwater. He yanked the rectangular-framed glasses from his face, pressed the thumb and forefinger of his opposite hand to the corners of his closed eyes. It was as though the gesture meant to push away not only the moment, this room, then me, but the widest stretch of memory. Replacing his glasses, Scott opened his eyes, gave in to the memory he could not shut out, and said: "Your handwriting... it amazes me. I almost can't look at it. It is exactly like my ex-fiancée's."

The next moment was perfectly still, dawn on that timeless desert. The first strands of sunlight that reached across the dark sky were equal parts child and parent, friend and lover entwining. But in what was, perhaps, the most oddly erotic moment of my life, Eros broke free, released his grip and hovered above the lot, plucking each strand of light. The melody strummed was unrecognizable, but the lyric was familiar to me as the opening lines of *In Search of Lost Time*. It was as though the thought eluding me only a moment before had come pouring out of Scott's own mouth. My words were his words, were the same words of Scott's ex-fiancée.

How had this happened? What exactly had happened? Had this ex-fiancée slid down a concealed rabbit hole? Was she dead? Or had she only slipped out of love? Why, that first day, when I saw Scott Matthews on an order card for a book called *On Love,* had I bothered to copy name and phone number so they would not be lost to me?—even before Scott walked into the shop and removed his dark glasses?

Scott went on to name the young woman he was to have married. Alive and well, her face and that of her mother sprang up in my mind's eye. I had known them for years, had watched the daughter grow from a pretty adolescent to a voluptuous young woman. And it came back to me: the last time I'd seen the pair in the shop had been about three years earlier. The daughter, blushing with sweetness (as if to give away their intimacy), had told me that she would soon be marrying "my Scottie." The mother, full of approval, had described him as a very nice young man. And now these two Scotties

—one private, one public—

merged before me in three-dimension, like converging images seen through the lens of a stereoscope.

I said to Scott, "I was going to show you this, then decided not to. Now I must. I believe it will help you with both your Proust and your ex-fiancée." I walked back over to the copy of *Buddhism Without Beliefs* that I'd previously marked. I then led Scott to the Bound Matters' Gold Customer Chair, as compatriot Al has come to calling it. It waits—wooden, worn, comfortable—and in its time has come to couch many of Summitt's citizens. Scott settled his threesome there—butt, mind, heart— as he quietly read three pages on the difficult topic of emptiness.

While he read I walked back over to the counter and stared at my own handwritten book list. I followed the curves of my script, traced the lines with my eye and tried to discern a parallel between them and the feminine curves of Scott's ex-fiancée.

When Scott had finished reading, he rejoined me at the counter. "Lots to think about there," he said, but my mind was elsewhere, and I asked, "So, who called off the marriage? She? Or you?"

"Oh," Scott answered, "I did. It was me. She wanted to go on living at home, her parents footing all the bills. Doesn't know how to take the next step. She's had several college majors and upon nearing completion of each, she switches to something else. I wanted to settle down with her, raise a family, but she postponed, postponed. It went on and on like that, each of us driving the other crazy. Finally, I grew tired of all the backtracking and delays and called it off. No going back."

"So you're another bit of her unfinished business."

"You could put it that way, yes."

"Falling in love," I said, "can be the most gawd-awful thing." And, of course, the unstated, most wonderful thing. Scott probably had no notion of what I was saying, of what I could not say when its saying was needed most. To embrace Scott, to kiss the boo-boo. But who can locate that spot? It isn't labeled "X" like the makeshift grave of a buried treasure. Nor is it that G spot or tenderloin between a man's legs so redundantly charted in all those expedient manuals. To this besieged grandmother's house there could be no shortcut. But there in the intricate loopholes of *In Search of Lost Time*, Marcel may have pointed the way. Where is that place his mother planted the long-awaited goodnight kiss? Could I not, Scott (though "Scott I'm not"), be your stand-in mom for this moment? To bend the rule here won't hurt a bit. And we needn't bother with distant affairs and broken engagements, but only this weird transference of emotions: Scott, naked as I would ever see him, showing me his still inconsolable grief—one man to another—and my now full-knowingly impossible love for him, broken off and left to dangle like live wires in an ice storm, crackling.

These are the words of words not said. But in the stillness of that desert dawn many things can be communicated in ways we are not aware, just as some of the best loves are never consummated in the conventional sense. And some of these remain the sweetest.

So goodnight, Marcel, my kiss in hand. Sweet dreams.

"I'll probably never see you again," I said to Scott as he was leaving the shop that morning.

"You'll see me again," he said, putting his hand out to shake mine. The custom concluded, he turned, and I watched the back of his white shirt disappear like a ghost through the shop door.

After he'd gone, I went to put back the copy of *Buddhism Without Beliefs* I'd had Scott read. Before putting it in its place, I absentmindedly flipped the book from back to front, and it fell open to two quotes prefacing the text. There, to my surprise, were the words of Marcel Proust. Full circle.

The words are:

> We do not receive wisdom, we must discover it for ourselves, after a journey through the wilderness, which no one can make for us, which no one can spare us, for our wisdom is the point of view from which we come at last to regard the world.

Ed

P.S. Tomorrow is the day the tell-all Presidential video is to be released, and I imagine the world will grow silent with its airing. It could be I lack the proper Family Values—but I fail utterly in seeing its importance. My business is elsewhere.

In love there can be no peace of mind.
—Marcel Proust

September 26, 1998

Dear Nancy,

Then comes the ache.

The fact that Scott had told me he was heterosexual, revealing even that special lost object of his desire, should have allowed me peaceably to put to rest the question of his orientation and pull myself happily out of love. But there was more to this mix of emotion than I could have guessed. It was as though the very moment I let my resistance down to the impossibility of the situation—that was the very same moment I was irretrievably lost to Scott.

I became a ridiculous, one-syllabled thing subject to the wildest swings of emotion. I wept easily. My appetite vanished. I slept poorly, if I slept at all. I began to get up in the middle of the night to write, and whatever it was that had happened to me pumped a range, an energy into my voice that hadn't been there before. The rest of my life might be going to Hell in a man's basket, but words flowed from me with the force of coursing spring water.

Otherwise I saw my actions as immature, and I admonished myself at every turn.

"Ed," I told myself, "you are behaving like a child."

"Ed, you know better than to let this kind of emotion get the upper hand."

"This is not appropriate."

"Why fall in love with a straight man when there are so many willing gay men about?"

But love is not to be directed like sheep before a collie. It has a gyroscopic device all its own that takes hold and leads. Thus no reasoning influenced my behavior, and in ways large and small I began to behave so like a fool that my only refuge came in learning how to laugh at myself. In the market, reaching for the sale brand of paper toweling, I noticed the higher-priced "Scott" brand next to it and reached for that instead. Books arriving at the shop were by Scott So-and-so, or a So-and-so Scott, were published by Scott, Foresman, were set in Scotland or Scottsdale. Every other automobile passing me in the street bore a plate that spoke of a "Scott" dealership. After placing my morning orders at the shop, I'd snap on the radio and the Royal Scottish Symphony would invariably strike up a tune inspired by the work of Sir Walter Scott. The name appeared everywhere. Why had I not fallen for someone called Nebuchadnezzar or Rumpelstiltskin?

On an unseasonably warm and humid day in September, when I should have lain low on my lunch hour, I decided I needed to go to the bank instead. I knew that Scott lived on a street called South Hardwick Avenue, which crossed Lanchester Pike just before Olde Money Savings and Loan. Why Olde Money should be in possession of my money is anyone's guess, but that is where my stash is kept.

I'd explored many of Summitt's streets before, but never South Hardwick. From its base on Lanchester Pike, it looks unappetizing with its gridlock of familiar franchises and chains, each built exactly the same as its inbred twin found at every other desirable location in a thousand other towns in America, assimilation in this way spelling the corruption of free enterprise and the death of creativity. So many sheep under the guidance of fewer and fewer collies. And in a town boasting many lovely churches, at the foot of South Hardwick is a homely, modern church so lacking in aesthetic charm it seems to say, "I have been designed by a clever architect oiled by a healthy budget; I did not grow by faith alone."

On that day the part I played insisted that I attend to the needless ritual of checking my bank balance, and I followed the script exactly as written. My worth assured, I left the bank, telling myself, "Oh!" as if surprised, "I think I'll forego the main route and take this street instead. It'll return me to the shop in no less time." My backstreet affair begun, I acted as though I was being watched—and watching too, like a stalker in a seedy film, the house full, every eye in the audience on me, its covert star. I was H. Humbert in pursuit of Lolita, Emma B. in spiraling decline, Anna K. caught between a hard husband and a handsome count—or best of all, and in keeping with the high standard of my lineage, I was M. Swann on the trail of Odette. My predecessors had not gotten what they wanted. Or, when they did, it was not what it had seemed. What then was it I wanted?

Knowing or not, I was driven on.

If our church was designed by that clever architect, then whoever had laid out the streets of Summitt must have been a drunken dyslexic. It's a senseless scribble, as if put down to deliberately confuse not only outsiders, but the locals as well. The Founding Fathers must have said to themselves, "Since we can't abide by Old World rules, putting in a moat and stocking it with hungry crocodiles, we'll create an ever-deceiving maze of streets." What they were trying to hide remains a mystery, but South Hardwick runs true to their directive. Adding to this routine confusion, fate played yet another trick on me that day. Since I'd told myself when I'd left the shop that I had no intention of walking up South Hardwick, I hadn't bothered to check Scott's address in the phone directory. My memory informed me that he lived at number 375, a residence I'd soon find elusive as that transient palace in the Aladdin story.

"It must be up here just fifty paces ahead," I told myself as I walked under a railway trestle strewn with graffiti. Graffiti? Unheard of in Summitt. I ignored the slovenly painted words, proceeding with the assignation: "It's not out of my way."

But what was this "it" anyway? An apartment, house, or brief stop on a previously uncharted Underground Railroad? Or was "it" that feeling burning and sparking in me like some kind of berserk Geiger counter measuring—what?—sperm count? Why should a homosexual give a piss about sperm count? I was behaving like a lunatic salmon on a spawning mission heading up the wrong stream.

Or was "it" that rigid wooden door on which to knock? A warm voice would respond, filtering through the swirl on the planking grain, saying "Welcome." And what had been unyielding would gently give way. But who am I kidding? If this were the case, I wouldn't need to be sneaking uninvited around South Hardwick. I know damn well as soon as Scott figured out why I was here and heard my "knock," the answer that would come would be "We don't want any."

But what did it matter? Whether my intended destination turned out to be a private residence, or the state-supported booby hatch where I might belong, Scott was busy selling business cards at his printshop, and I was a leisured passerby on a street in a country where freedom is not an abstract concept.

As if that street had heard, it exercised its freedom and veered sharply to the left, away from the bookshop, the house numbers turning at a mockingly sluggish pace: 153...155...157.... But I liked the look of things. The street was quiet, laid back, the houses small and unpretentious. Scott didn't have to pretend he was some wealthy Main Liner and live, over-mortgaged, with more bedrooms than he needed. One would do nicely. And when my "knock" on that bedroom door came, the voice inside would say, "It's okay. Come in. I know you're not soliciting. You've only something to tell me."

A car approached me from behind and began to slow up. I stared straight ahead, affecting nonchalance, though sensing I was under surveillance. As my peripheral vision sharpened, the car continued to slow until it pulled up beside me, its pace matching my own. Turning toward it, I saw the window on the driver's side was down. "Oh-oh," I thought, the car coming to a near-dead halt. "That driver knows I'm on an illicit mission." My heart sounded in my ears, an apparent drum roll announcing the censure I was about to hear. "Yes, " the driver would say, "he does live here. But you've no business in this fine neighborhood. Go back to the wicked city where you belong."

But the driver remained silent, only the rev of his engine sounding. The car then lurched forward and sped away, revealing the joke that had been played upon me. This was one of those quiet residential streets where someone had planted a bump in the pavement so that each driver needs to slow or sends his skull crashing through the hood of his car. Seeing that bump—a bit of raised asphalt and tar—I heard the Founding Fathers laughing at me, saying: "You'll never get away with this. Not a single homosexual lives on this street. Zoning laws forbid it."

Now I know these Founding Fathers to be a bunch of charlatans, trapped in time and crackpot, and I laughed, too. Zoning laws are never spoken, but kept quiet, locked away, the keys misplaced. So I pooh-poohed the whole of my paranoia and walked jauntily, surefootedly ahead, applying new lyrics to an old tune: "I have never walked down this street before, so this pavement's never been beneath my feet before. All at once have I so many stories t' tell—it is Hell on the street where you live."

I was clever as the cleverest architect. Patrick would be proud. And one day, while guiding a bunch of doddering, well-heeled Presbyterians through the Great Churches of Italy, dog-eared Baedeker's under arm, I would expire in Venice. Dispensing with the funeral, the weeping, and the neatly dug grave, they will instead pitch my body into the Grand Canal, there to wash out to sea. Free at last, free at last. Thank Oscar, bless Tennessee that I might at last be free.

I smiled with renewed assurance as I lustfully eyed the street numbers turning, swiftly now as I reached my goal: 367...369...371.

I stopped.

The last number was 373. Then the street ran out, ended at an intersection, and stubbornly refused to continue. I couldn't tell if the titters I heard came from my movie audience or those damnable Founding Fathers. So I dismissed them both with a great wave of my hand. *All nonsense*, I concurred with myself, then asked, "What is becoming of my lunch hour? Must be halfway to Villa Nouveau Riche by now and haven't even acquired a sandwich."

I glanced to the right, didn't like what I saw, so turned left and walked up to the next street. "South Northumberland Circle," the sign read.

Where is 375? I muttered, the stink of my own sweat mixing with panic.

I backtracked to see what street crossed in the other direction. Another blind alley, again no South Hardwick. There was a great stone house presiding on the edge of a park. It was surrounded by those little signs stuck into the ground that seem to say "Protected by..." but actually say, "I have something worth taking." In the driveway sat a large dog, snoozing. Just in case the alarm system was down, here was a backup with a good set of teeth.

"Do you know where Scott lives?" I thought to ask him. The dog awakened, raised his head and gave me the eye, looking all the more menacing, ever larger. Well, I'd seen two male dogs getting it on often enough. He'd probably be more understanding than that man in the car only minutes before. My mission is not a dirty thing, I thought: I am in love.

Unexpectedly, the dog's tail began to beat friendily against the pavement.

"Yes," he was saying. "I'm fond of Scott, too. He comes by often, and he's into very heavy petting."

I shook my head, the prospect of a little canine affection suddenly tinged with the erotic. My stomach turned. I am *ridiculous*, accent on the dick.

I must cease at once, turn back before I do something I will regret. It's only appropriate that Scott's house seems to have evaporated. I've no business there. And somewhat bewildered, my puppy lover's tail shriveling before me, I retreated to the safety of the bookshop. There the liaisons are straightforward, climactic, and kept quietly locked between covers.

So you see it's not mere rumor: the course of true love has never been smooth. Not for poor Emma and Anna, not for H. Humbert or M. Swann. Certainly not for me. Not even, it would seem, for Scott.

Ed

P.S. Is friendily a word? It isn't in my pocket dictionary. Still, I think it works.

September 30, 1998

Dear Nancy,

Returning to the shop, I got out the local phone directory, opened it, and discovered the error of my house hunt: Scott's residence was number 365. The directory slipped from my hands and dropped with a thud to the floor, its pages turning until the book fell quietly shut. Staring at the thing, I realized I would have to find some way to vent my feelings. Otherwise, I might find myself wandering the labyrinth of Summitt's streets for eternity, a clueless mummy wrapped in reams of decaying Scott tissue. *Who knows where this sort of thing might lead?*

So on September 8th, 1998, I sat down and composed a brief letter to Scott. I proceeded with calm detachment, any deception meant to fall away, like excess baggage on the road to enlightenment. Employing the simple and direct philosophy of a well-known writer's manual, I drew on recent shared events and the distant memories they'd evoked. Checking my wanton drives at the door, I recognized them for what they were: rattled emotions belonging to the Jiffy-pop of infatuation. Hot enough to melt butter, then quick to cool.

This aside, Scott and I were two clear-thinking adults. After all, Scott was about to embark upon the great adventure of *A la recherche du temps perdu*, the intellectual equivalent of a trek to the South Pole. If you go and you come back, you do not come back the same. You may even come back missing a digit or two. But Scott was not unaware. He was prepared for the journey and would likely return with all extremities in working order.

My problem was that I'd become such an assimilated, nearly invisible gay man in a predominantly hetero world that I had almost forgotten it is important, now and then, to stick out your sore thumb and let it be known what is up. Mind you, I would not be graphic. Scott might be mature, he might even have sprouted a gray pubic hair or two, but he had absolutely no interest in having sex with another man. He lacked the gene. I knew this by the look that came onto his face when I'd pointed to my handwritten book list and he'd remembered his ex-fiancée. A man can more easily fake an orgasm than to fake such a look. But Scott wasn't narrow-minded. Simply because he tended the conventional pasture did not mean he was oblivious to what happens on the other side of the fence. Partake? *Never!* Scott didn't even rank a casual browser. But why should he mind hearing how I'd giddily strayed up South Hardwick Avenue? The mainspring of our union was a good story. Surely my fevered walk qualified.

But once I put pen to yellow sheets, all this would prove idle research. Under the weight of a squadron of Rube Goldberg contraptions, my upright epistle first buckled, then collapsed. The Ink Dispenser, The Stamp Affixer, The Page Turner—they marched across the bridge of our handshake like soldiers programmed by their commander, the entire battalion to be filed under the heading:

The Ass Licker!

Figuratively speaking, of course, the setup so designed that a gay man might concede he'd fallen for a straight man—but without letting him in on the secret. Hand on my internal Bible, it was truth I meant to tell. Instead I reached for the knob of the cold water faucet and let the tap run full blast, the resulting gesture limp as some people's wrists. My performance was about as anatomically correct as plastic Ken, minus Barbie, yes, but whose only appendage which might sport a condom is that same place Bartholomew Cubbins had donned any one of his five-hundred hats. What followed in my wake was not a stream of colorful headgear, but a camouflaged dribble spelling:

sexless, heartless, coy, dishonest

—each conspiring to undo what is best about friendship. And unlike another situation where friendship is not the end desire, here it would be written in big, burning letters, the bond no less a miracle than the unscorched trio of Shadrach, Meshach, and Abednego.

But no miracle would come of the letter I had written, a cute little aberration of truth full of coded messages Scott would not see. I put it through the Rube Goldberg contraptions, mailed it via the Rube Goldberg post, and waited—quite impatiently—for a response. None came. An entire week passed. Had that speed reader Scott, who'd consumed de Botton titles with relish as though they were hors d'oeuvres, suddenly hit a blind spot? Or had I, thinking I'd boldly cracked some omelet-bound eggs, succeeded only in laying one?

I remained an uncomfortable hen until I heard the news that Edmund White had written a slender monograph on Marcel Proust to be published in January 1999. This gave me what I took to be a legitimate excuse to phone Scott. I did, leaving a message on his machine which concluded, "and how is your reading group coming along with the standard of French literature?"

The following morning, as if to resume our mating pattern, Scott arrived at the bookshop in virginal white. I was no longer taken in. He'd received several distressed emails from other members of the group, each bogged down in the Overture to *Swann's Way*:

"What's going on here?"

"I don't get it."

"I'm lost."

Comments like that. No surprise to me. I had tried to warn Scott. But, of course, my curiosity about the progress of the reading group was a decoy. My genuine concern was with *my* email, old-fashioned variety, hand job. Had *that* gotten through?

"Yes," Scott nodded eagerly, it had. But only in the most prosaic way. Scott was appreciative. He said I wrote well and that he'd liked what I had to say. But I wasn't fishing for a compliment or auditioning for a position at *The New York Times*. If position it was, it was for that open, deepening friendship which meant that not only might we read Proust in our separate cubicles, but pursue our own rendition of time lost and found.

"Ed," Scott then asked, "do you think you might join our reading group? You could be a big help."

The temptation to say "yes" here was greater than at any other time in my remembered past, but I only hesitated a moment before giving Scott my stock answer. "As a bookseller I feel it would be incestuous to join a reading group when I am supplying the books. Go find yourself a clerk at...."

Scott smiled, the sparkle of his pearly teeth a perfect mate to his shirt, and said, "So what's wrong with a little incest?"

Perhaps I'd misjudged the boy.

But as our conversation continued, I saw that my email had been lost on Scott. How was it this compulsive reader of even the most difficult fiction stumbled on a single slender letter? It was as though the language of a gay man and the language of a straight man were two distinct dialects, each beyond the ear of the other. And as the words of my now-dead letter settled squarely on my reluctant shoulders, I felt the full weight of Bartholomew Cubbins' five-hundred hats.

What had I done?

I'd made an aloof reference to a popular film, *The Crying Game*. I'd misquoted dear Mrs. Madrigal in *Tales of the City*, saying she'd said, "There are all kinds of families" when it was actually "all kinds of marriages." My unconscious had bent the aphorism to fit the situation, for although Scott might accept me as a member of his extended family, he'd never consent to anything resembling marriage. I had, it's true, mentioned a broken romance, but had left my ex genderless and nameless. And all these anagrammed crumbs I'd sent floating in the tea-warm liquid of Marcel Proust, that gayest of all literary icons after Whitman, and hero to boot. Unlike E.M. Forster, who forbade publication of *Maurice* until after his death, Proust allowed *Sodom and Gomorrah* to appear in his own lifetime. And he had *nothing* to do with camouflaging the title in its subsequent translations.

But Scott hadn't gotten any of this.

"We are simply incompatible!" I shouted again to myself. "I've fallen for a dope."

But wait. Whose hand was it that scrambled the puzzle pieces? Not Scott's, my long-silent partner still wedded to a muddle no one dares subvert. And how each generation passes it to the next, the most recent update being the ludicrous vow of:

> Don't ask.
> Don't tell.

Might as well cross the threshold into a house of mirrors. It was up to me to begin the annulment. I had learned in childhood, in the fevered awakenings of adolescence, even in what I took to be a more open adulthood, to disguise the better part of me—and I have never entirely forgotten how the game is played. Centuries of the residue stinks in lost time, and Scott, in his own way, remains just as closeted. It would seem that unless I dress like Liberace, speak like Truman Capote, and get down on my knees and beg to give head, I will not be understood. But what had a costume, a manner of speech, or the particulars of a sexual act to do with what was happening here?

> *Nothing.*

I'd found myself groping through the dense fog of mourning over Patrick and had happened upon Scott. Or else it was Scott who had come stumbling out of his long engagement onto me. Or was it that each of us, on opposite ends of a twenty-five-year stretch, had come spinning off a broken romance onto Proust? Whichever it was, we'd both been set down in a labyrinth not of our own making where the guards at the gates were as dizzied as the inmates. And within that benighted complex of passages had appeared a veil, always there, once transparent as a scrim let down between stage and audience, its lifting long overdue.

Gay people could be the main characters in a hit play, the brunt of a joke, or someone coming out during prime time. But always someone held at a fictional distance, not the first person Scott might see in the morning—whether it be turning over in bed or discovering a bookshop open at an unexpected hour. How had I not seen it before? For the sake of that sweet friendship left waiting in the wings, each of us would need to endure the critical fire of opening night. And were the premiere a sell-out, or the house half-empty, I would have to pin Scott down to the mat of our troubles until he hollered "Uncle!" Until he saw that love in all its many splintered variations could come in unexpected packages. There is no inappropriate place for it, there is only the inappropriate expression of it.

So while Scott gabbled on about Proust, his reading group, and the virtues of my old-fashioned email, I considered how I would form my proposal. I would ask the father of the bride his permission—Scott being the father, the bride being his friendship—permission to dismantle the Rube Goldberg, to take down the walls of that labyrinth, to let the light flood into Miss Havisham's bridal suite. When I had sorted this out in my head, and Scott paused to catch his breath, I asked him a question I don't remember my ever having asked another human being.

"Scott. Are you my friend?"

"Yes, of course," he answered.

But the answer wasn't enough, and so I asked:

"Scott, can I confide in you?" Again, the answer I heard was: "Yes."

But still it wasn't enough, and so I asked:

"Can I trust you?"

"Yes."

I heard this stream of conscious yeses as any bookseller might, its repeated affirmations a match to the gushy climax, all perfume and breasts, of what many call the 20th century's greatest novel, James Joyce's *Ulysses*.

Of course, Scott and I would be keeping our breasts to ourselves, but my bosom buddy had given me something of equal importance. He had bestowed upon me a triple crown of yeses. Now our friendship would swell as in a pregnancy. Scott was to become my trusted confidant, twisted recipient of my tattered tale, and the word *friend* glowed from within anew. All the Magi of my life had guided me to this single starlit point in time.

But had I heard it correctly or was this only my own fantasy put upon Scott? Does he hear himself correctly, or is the word *friend* for Scott as disposable as the articles *a* or *an*?

Amy.

There. I have said it: not just ex-fiancée, but *Amy*, a name with its own sound, distinct and small-syllabled. *Amy*, meaning "loved" or "beloved," the perfect pet name

—no!—

pen name for the person who had been Scott's most intimate companion. Amy is yet another dope in this o-so-human comedy, its turns clever enough to evoke envy in the greatest bard. Amy said "no" even as she performed many of the yeses I might be pleased to perform, but cannot—and put them out of my head as swiftly as they appear. And when Scott, in winner-take-all-or-nothing positioning, could not have the all of Amy till death do they part, he said "no" to her. Now Scott at a loose end has given me not one but three yeses—and it could be *Cliffs Notes* will be required to follow this plot to climax.

It was a rule inviolate of romance novelist Barbara Cartland that no sex should take place until the final page. In truth the details were left to the space beyond, and ultimately the imagination of the reader—encouraging what I have long believed, that the brain is our largest sex organ.

It may be that Scott and I were destined from the first to board a final empty page. So here we *must* go, our small craft astride waters dark as the river Styx. Together we must go and lift a veil neither of us had seen was there.

It is clear that the truth I seek is not in him, but in me. He has awakened it.
—Marcel Proust,
A la recherche du temps perdu

October 2, 1998

Dear Nancy,

In the days that immediately followed, armed with Scott's yeses but not without trepidation, I renewed my epistolary journey under the title, "How Scott Aaron Matthews Can Change Your Life." And these letters I dutifully sent, one by one, to their unwitting recipient.

At first the ache seemed only to increase. Did even a third yes give me the freedom to flaunt such a freshly won friendship? Was I an unwanted missionary imposing a new thought when the old ones had apparently been doing fine for centuries? Or was I needlessly extending the pain of what could only be called unrequited love? The answer that came to such inquiry was an odd one: this is NOT unrequited love. I could neither understand the answer, nor could I say with any certainty from where it came. "It" didn't seem concerned so long as "I" proceeded. Thus, under a self-imposed oath to tell the whole truth (and who but the likes of a Proust has ever succeeded in that?), I went on.

I remembered that Scott had paid for all but one of his books on a green American Express card. My internal Bible had proven to be an infernal one, but now, to sharpen the accuracy of my account, I got out all the shop records of these transactions. I saw that they informed me of more than the amount of each purchase and the titles involved. Here was a brief tally of all the time Scott and I had spent together, and this I calculated to be about an hour and a half. Ninety minutes. Such a little bit of time. How could such a little bit of time be wreaking so much havoc in my life? How, exactly, does a person "fall in love" in a mere ninety minutes? Again the answer that was returned was an odd one: he does not. He falls in that incalculable nanosecond where his emotional guard is down. Or else, in full charge of his reason, he turns and slips through a chink in time, glimpsing Eden again the way a time traveler might. It begins in bliss blossoming, but the ache, which spontaneously follows, comes of the knowledge that however perfect the potential union may be, whatever is gotten in life will one day be lost. Eternity balks at even the mention of proprietorship, and in love, especially, beginning and ending meet head-on in a flash blinding as any atomic detonation.

But on the backstroke of a reprimand, I reminded myself that Scott and I are about as far from the distant couple of Adam and Eve as we are from the date of their fall, and that I had become absurd as that player in the story about the Polish lesbian who falls in love with a man. Scott thinks of me only when he walks through the shop door and stops thinking of me when he exits. He has quickly moved into my consciousness, furniture and all. I don't pass through any door without the hope of meeting him in the next room.

This is how I found myself in the retelling: hemming and hawing, continuously cursing myself for having allowed such a thing to happen—then moving forward again, knowing forward is the only true direction. Forget East, West, North, and South, those lame illusions wrought by cartographers under the spell of gravity. The answer to my every question in this new line of work was always the unexpectedly odd one. All previous assumptions needed revision.

In Gay Liberation 101, the young man learns it is prohibited to fall in love with a heterosexual male. Nothing wrong with a distanced admiration of physique, just don't put any emotional stock in it. It is a waste. But isn't one of the primary lessons of love always something transcendent, often impractical, unearthly, or rather, something so keenly in tune with everything on this earth that it seems to make the workaday world a humdrum? From the vantage point of the lover, everyone else's life appears a pitiful routine of the same old, same old—the very light, the very color around him switching from early Manet to late Monet.

The Rube Goldberg dropped away, an unwieldy piece of equipment outmoded by new technology, and a cleaner machine was set in motion.

I'd tumbled into that billionth of one second, a crack so small no one could take credit for what happens there, and no order handed down by the legal profession could point to the responsible party. Outside all jurisdiction, it is as much an Act of God as a tidal wave, a hurricane. And whether the big wind goes by the hardy name of Scott or a feminine diminutive, its gender, too, belongs to those antiquated maps, waters spotted with sea monsters, their open mouths implying:

"Too far."

All lessons of gay liberation, from kindergarten to graduate school, now lent credence to that oft-spoken divide existing between academic and real worlds: I was no longer in school. In flouting some rule, by toying with a taboo, I'd been sent down, expelled. And the heavy rock of my punishment would go on matching the steep incline that had been my crime. Stuck in love with someone I could never hope to possess, I felt very much like I was seventeen years old, returned to a time when I was not so much as supposed to exist.

But, remember? Eternity balks at proprietorship, can hold onto nothing unless it concedes to letting it go. The single true direction is forward, and in pursuing it, I would find the way, only this time it could not be through any usual door frame. The metaphor of the closet had outlived its purpose for me too many years before, and Scott could do little more than imagine that place. Now he would need to be a part of this oddly latent transition involving us both. By holding a looking glass up to Scott, I would force him to peer into his own steel-blue eyes exactly as I had. For the moment he would be lost there, too, and the discomfort would force him to seek a way out. But he wouldn't exit alone, would need to be tricked into taking my hand then. Not for the brief wag of a handshake, or to fulfill any sexual inclination. Rather for the purpose of some deeper thing existing behind all such activity, that thing we fear is not there (so that we grope at loins all the more), but is only a dreamer's notion done up in a sweet-scented Valentine, there to mask the rotting bowels of a long-dead god.

It was at this moment I realized it was not Scott Aaron Matthews who had changed my life, but Marcel Proust. Without knowing it, with no awareness of the undertow, Scott had succeeded in taking me back. For the sake of all those extant variations of "don't ask, don't tell," I was now obligated to take the two of us forward. Thus we were linked.

One morning, in the midst of all this hemming and hawing, I woke at four and even before coming into full consciousness broke into sobs. These were so great that the whole of my body heaved. The sobs went on, off and on, for the better part of the morning, and they were greater by far than any I'd spent on Patrick.

This jarring frightened me so that I thought I might be suffering from clinical depression. Barely hours before, I'd found myself in what I thought was a euphoria induced by love. Might these be instead the pit-and-pendulum swings of manic-depression?

I spoke to a clinical psychologist I knew casually from the shop. In a similar fashion, I'd spoken to this same man the summer after Patrick's death, when I felt so numb I couldn't cry. He'd assured me then that one day I would experience great and unexpectedly sudden emotional upheavals, that the reactions to suicide especially involve denial and the postponement of the mourning process.

"There is no set clock for this process," he'd said. "It is different for each person and situation."

The day of upheaval at hand, I mentioned the possibility of clinical depression, and he asked:

"Going to work?"

"Yes," I answered, "of course."

"Paying your bills?"

"Yes."

"Dealing with people? You *are* talking with me."

"Yes, sure." Another trio of yeses had appeared on my doorstep.

"If you were clinically depressed," I was told, "you probably couldn't do any of those things, much less to juggle all three. Remind yourself that it's only been little more than a year since Patrick's death. Relax, Ed. Bend to your sorrow or you'll break."

Okay. The steadying hand of a professional had put the question to rest: I was not ill. Perhaps I should get it in writing, put it on a banner and parade it with the Mummers come New Year's:

MY SOBS ARE ONLY ANOTHER
MOON PHASE OF MOURNING.

But I was not a good patient. I mentioned only my sobs, made no reference to Scott and the euphoria accompanying his arrival. Patrick was so little on my mind at that moment it is a wonder that when the psychologist spoke his name I did not ask, "Patrick who?"

Had I told my makeshift doctor about the awkward situation with Scott and what I was doing to resolve it, I feared he would laugh at me and say something like, "Why, you're not ill at all. You're simply in love. And judging from that look, you've got it bad. You say he's not gay? Do you know how queer it is for a gay man to fall for a straight man? It's just plain perverted."

I didn't need to hear him say that. This was one diagnosis I could make on my own.

The way out for Scott came one morning when I reached the bookshop and saw that an envelope with my name on it had been slid through a crack in the heavy glass door. Not my full name, mind you, just Ed. Rhymes with dead. And Scott hadn't even bothered to waste a stamp on me. The eagle had landed, "Uncle!" had arrived.

I put my key in the door, opened it, and bent down to pick up the envelope with the lone syllable on it. It didn't take anything like clairvoyance to discern what would be inside. The news would be bad. I had drifted to the wrong side of the buck fence and the enclosed was my penalty for having trespassed. Scott had received the second installment of "How Scott Aaron Matthews Can Change Your Life." I'd put the third in the mail the morning before, and he would be receiving it later this same day. Having whittled Bartholomew Cubbins' hat collection down to a precious few, I was about to reveal the big one. Scott would react like the man in *The Crying Game* when he discovers his date has a dick. He goes to the toilet and vomits. A perfectly natural response to such an unnatural thing. Emily Post would advise the same—and be sure to have a hanky handy to mop up any mess.

I braced myself for the stink of the upchuck, opened the envelope, and read the contents.

September 20, 1998

Dear Ed,

I've been thinking for the past couple hours how to correctly and delicately address the problem you have presented me. Unfortunately the right words won't come to mind. Please forgive my insensitivity...if that is how I sound.

It would appear that I have misled you, Ed. Forgive me if that is what has happened. Let me make it clear that I have no interest whatsoever in relationships with men other than that of friendship, and I am surprised you think otherwise.

You haven't told me that you think I'm gay, but what else could you think, given the nature of the letters you've written? Except for the first, when I had no idea of the nature of your interest in me, your letters have made me quite uncomfortable. Although I am certain that is not your intention, I must ask you to stop.

Hopefully, my visiting the store in the future will not bother you. If you would prefer, I could drop by in the evenings when I need something. Please let me know.

Sincerely,
Scott

Bother me? How could Scott ever bother me?

I let the hand that held the letter drop sadly to my side. There was a ringing in my ears. Either the room had taken to turning round me or my head was spinning like a globe on its axis—I couldn't tell which. The thought of never seeing Scott again was sending me into a panic. I read the note a second time and saw, as I'd not the first, that Scott had given me the option, asking if I would prefer that he come into the shop in the evenings when he knew I wasn't there.

PERMISSION DENIED.

Did Scott think I was a slam-bam-thank-you-ma'am kind of guy, so pushy and always in need of having my own way? That because our friendship had this bittersweet twist—like the sliver of a lemon rind Patrick would slip into his martini before he gave up the ritual entirely and took to drinking the stuff straight from the bottle—because of that, our friendship was to be abandoned at once? How could I rectify the damage done? Fully knowing he was straight, I'd risked our potential friendship by telling Scott who I really am. I'd not written those letters as a pathway to a proposition, or because I believed Scott was gay. In fact, here I'd thought was the perfect opportunity to build a friendship with a man where sex could not screw things up—but damn if it hadn't screwed things up anyway. I should've listened to the commonsense advice, that a gay man must never express affection for a straight man. It's an offense reprehensible as child molestation. But I did know, knew full well, why I'd not listened: I simply don't believe in it, am incapable of believing in it. That tired advice is poppycock belonging to the dust bin, not the status quo. Each life is made a little poorer for it. *The entire world is made a poorer place for it.*

What I loved about being with Scott was the comfort he brought with him. Whenever he walked into a room, I felt more at home than before. When he left, any number of strangers couldn't fill the space. That is what it means to have a friend—their very presence is home, their absence a void compounding. *So how is it*, I repeated, *Scott could ever bother me*? I was able to tell him anything. But then I saw: problem and telling are one, *indivisible*. That word I would recite daily in grade school, not knowing what it meant. And while its meaning shone clear through this fledgling pledge of allegiance, the affection behind the word had begun to percolate in too plain a view. Dear Sam I Am, it was *unmanly*.

I phoned Scott's business and got an answering machine with Scott's taped voice stating the hours the printshop was open. When the message had played and the long

"beeep"

sounded, I opened my mouth, but no word would come. My tongue and the walls that housed it went instantly dry upon contact with the air. Again the room took to swinging around me. I hung up the phone. Even if I could have found the words, what might I have said that wouldn't have revealed my feelings to anyone else who heard the message?

So I phoned Scott at his home. Another taped message, another long

"beeep."

Soon the world would have no use for real people but would be reduced to a tower of babbling taped messages and beepers echoing in an empty sky. Still I did manage to find some words on the occasion of this second

"beeep,"

and I said:

"Hello, Scott. This is Ed. Who else would it be on *this* morning? Everything is fine. *Don't* worry about it. You've done nothing to be apologizing about, and I've done nothing to be sorry about. We haven't DONE anything. It just happened, and how could I go on calling you friend if I didn't figure some way of telling you?" I trailed off, my words collapsing under me like the legs of a runner after a marathon. This was as close to phone sex as I'd ever come, and it felt strange talking so passionately to a machine. It was surely very different from my usual telephone message of "Hello, whoever the hell you might be, your book is in!"

As soon as the time came for Scott's printshop to open, I phoned it again. The wait was similar, I imagined, to that first hour after having received a terminal diagnosis, the alternate verdict of a second opinion not yet available. Receiver pressed to my ear, I heard the ringing on the other end, a click, and the same taped message I'd listened to before, followed by the third long

"beeep"

of the morning. It screeched in my head like the wail of a banshee, moving with lightning speed from that fevered climax of *Ulysses* to the opening scream of *Gravity's Rainbow*. Then a woman, the genuine article, came on the line. The real voice made me feel like someone found drifting at sea. I clutched the lifeline, told the voice my name and asked what time Scott Matthews was expected. She didn't know. She would go to find out. I was put on hold. In the few seconds of silence I drifted back out to sea. Then Scott's voice came unexpectedly on the line.

"Hello, Ed!"

In an instant I'd been propelled from mid-ocean to bedrock Canadian Shield. The voice was not my vomiting date, but beckoned instead, as if Scott were putting out his arm over the telephone line to shake my hand. The note had been a mistake. First chance, I'd tear it to bits. Gone were the dark waters punctuated with sea monsters, in its place an open door of yeses that said:

"Go on."

"Scott," I began, repeating the phrase I'd blurted less coolly into his answering machine. "Everything is fine. This has to be awkward right now. Awkward for both of us. But I can't—I cannot just stop. Had I seen where things were going at the beginning, I'd have done things different. But who can do that? It's a crazy situation, but what's to be ashamed of?"

Scott seemed to accept what I was saying, but was unable to say much in response, so I went on as though speaking for the two of us.

"And it's best this way. It simply is this way and no other. You didn't mislead me. And I am trying my hardest not to mislead you. There's no reason in the world why you might not have been gay—but you aren't. And I wasn't looking to be in love with anyone right now, so that leaves us both off the hook."

Scott laughed.

"Now we don't have to go through some long, complicated affair," I went on, speculating, "where we spend months ironing out the details, sexual or otherwise, then end by having a nasty breakup. We're the lucky ones. We've had our nasty breakup right at the beginning."

Scott laughed again.

"We've broken a mold and can now become the good friends we're meant to be. You'll see it all the more clearly in the next letter. And because I mailed it yesterday, you'll know it wasn't written as a compromise to your note asking me to stop. How can I stop what was begun here?"

I don't know how much sense I was making, but I again felt very much at home. What ought to have been one of the most difficult conversations of my life came easily to me. And I could feel the smile in Scott's accepting voice, the cool blue eyes and the crisp white shirt. Our worst moment behind us, my eviction papers had been scrapped and thrown to the fire. Hanging up the phone for the third time that morning, there in the dying flames, I watched an unlikely menage à trois: Shadrach, Meshach, and Abednego. The accompanying music was faint and indistinct, but I think I recognized the step. It may have been the light fandango, a waltz, or a more passionate tango. Or, no, most likely of all: a Scottish reel.

Ed

And the day came when the risk it took to remain closed in a bud became more painful than the risk it took to blossom.
—Anaïs Nin

October 6, 1998

Dear Nancy,

Scott and I had both erred. I, perhaps, on the side of love. He out of fear and inexperience, but not intolerance. My instincts about Scott had been good, but we'd lacked a blueprint, had no precedent to guide us along. This wasn't about something arbitrary as political affiliation, which church each of us happened to attend, or what either might like on his half of a shared pizza. This wasn't even about the relatively simple notion of sexual preference. This was about meeting head-on a situation usually avoided, about maneuvering a friendship between Scylla and Charybdis.

At its onset, falling for Scott had been like any infatuation, the dynamics of an air bag expanding upon contact, quickly deflated. Then, when I began to perceive the depths of my feelings, a shame came over me, as if I had betrayed my own people. But whether I went on chumming with my own tribe, or flipped alliances and chummed with another—still there was no one in either camp to whom I could tell what had happened. And this not telling seemed to be eroding my reason. Having located a crack in that darkness—"Dear Nancy" suspended in cold waters of mourning—I then turned what had been intended for Nancy onto Scott. At first this twisted epistle seemed only to pull me deeper into my quagmire. On those sleepless nights and restless days that soon followed, I'd imagined that I'd broken a time-honored code, even that I might be committing a crime. But all I'd really done was to deconstruct the Rube Goldberg so that Scott could better see the entirety of his world and I could breathe more easily in it. There would be no headline in *The Summit Sun*: "Local Bookseller Found Dead of Broken Heart. Proust Implicated. Printer May Be Linked." That would have been as premature as "Dewey Defeats Truman."

You might conclude, because Eros could never be entirely left out of my feelings for Scott, that this unlikely affair had come to an unhappy ending. But it had not ended, nor was I unhappy. I would say instead that I was finding new ways to reconstruct Eros so that he would not do our friendship any harm.

Masturbation is that activity, unforgettable as learning to ride a bicycle, that probably has more to do with the relative sanity of this world than has lithium. For now it would have to do. The interesting thing I found in this was that I could not do it and think about Scott at the same time. Try, and I short-circuited. But this only served to confirm the well of feeling he'd opened in me. Even there in the privacy of my own room, the door locked and the world shut out, my erotic imagination was unable to cheat on love. It informed me:

"Find another way."

I was also realizing that coming out—the phrase borrowed from a passé social passage—wasn't the isolated act I'd imagined before, but more on the order of an alcoholic's recovery. Not a snapshot moment commemorated with a fancy-dress ball, but process itself. Heterosexuality is an assumption imposed until a replacement is stated. Being homosexual is a declaration you must be seen to make, again and again. I suppose I'd forsaken my process in those early, oh-so confusing days of AIDS, when sex became dangerous and love remained the same pain in the butt it's always been. I took the easy way and abstained. Still, I couldn't walk out on a world that had become a second home for me, and there witnessed too many friends long since abandoned by their first families. Like Pinocchio en route from wood to flesh, they'd found comfort on a remote isle inhabited wholly by boys. And these sad beauties in their heated prime, I watched them slowly drop, one sad beauty at a time.

Since I'd managed to sidestep the plague, perhaps my punishment from God was to fall for Scott. *Let the punishment fit the crime!* It forced me to resume my process at the place I'd left off, and more: to question the status quo in a way I'd not dared before. It was likely a function of love that made me think for an instant my confessor would go untroubled by my confession. But the morning Scott's note appeared at the shop door, I saw the Monet colors drain from the picture. Years of apparent change had grown into decades, yet the trinity of yeses was about to evaporate like a politician's word. Here in the land of family values there could be only one valued family, each husband, each wife greedily clinging to their marriage contract. Those refusing to align themselves with the status quo were still damned to some third-world ghetto, nameless, threatening. And not by their maker, who made them all, but by their fellow countrymen.

As one with them, Scott had done what most any straight man does when a gay man gets too close: he closes the door, backs off, doesn't want to hear about it. *Who knows?* There may be some sleight-of-hand connection between thinking about a homosexual or having a homosexual think about you—and then becoming one yourself. Hadn't Scott written in his note: "You haven't told me you think I'm gay, but what else could you think?"

What else? I wanted to fling my words the way a wolf slings howls at an indifferent moon. There is so much else to think, an inner territory more in need of charting than was this outer one when Columbus stumbled on it. And what wonder the grounds remain riddled with live landmines? The charges will not, they cannot undo themselves.

Sure. So long as the reservation-bound kept quiet, Scott would go on behaving like the good Scott, armed with a steady kindness that followed through like his handshake. The simplicity of the gesture, the welcoming palm, warm smile, beckoning eyes, and steaming coffee. The world that is Proust opening up again before me like a yawn teasing oxygen to the brain—all had helped to bring me back to life. And I in turn had felt a need to inform Scott of what his kindness had wrought. A little more than he'd bargained for, but far, far less than he would encounter along the road of *In Search of Lost Time.*

But the story I was conveying was not safely sleeved between the covers and glossy jacket of a novel penned long before either of us had been born. In allowing the jugular of my story to pump with living fluid, I'd gone further by remaining closer. And had I asked any outsider for advice, I imagine the advice I'd have gotten would have been:

"Forget it."

But it is they who have forgotten "it."

For once I held the memory of love not as I did my dick in my own hand, but at its source. It had lost all concern with the particulars of anatomy. There in the dark wood I'd come to, only Scott's love would do, and by love here I mean little more than his acceptance. But while this had been a story sprung of a love that once dared not speak its name, now it would speak with daring enough to put the love of lesser stories to shame.

The Forbidden City in China contains 9,999 rooms because, its inhabitants held, only Heaven could contain ten thousand. In the pure light of that moment, I stood at the threshold of the ten-thousandth room—and the door swung open. And when Scott attempted to close that door and the apparently fragile basket dropped, eggs and all crashing to the hardest of surfaces, I'd closed my eyes in the noisy panic of the moment. No volume, *not seven volumes,* of rejection could pull this faith out from under me; nothing fallible as a marriage contract could contain it.

I became the source.

And when I opened my eyes, I saw the memory of love was still whole, unbroken. Nothing Scott could say or do would alter it.

To suggest that even a single person cannot so much as seek a way to say

"I love you"

is to drain the entirety of love from the world. But if it were only one who has been so deprived, then for the sake of that one, the rest of the world must be kept waiting. We are at love together or we are nowhere at all. And the same romantic love that brings with its isolation an ache and a loneliness will—in its maturity—abolish that ache, dispense with that loneliness. It can bear its solitude and wait for the rest of the world to catch up with it.

"It" may go by many names, be called nirvana, the light of Christ, or the awakening of Buddha. Or "it" may be that perfect moment going by no name but that each of us has felt in the quiet of a sunlit morning.

Or, in the words of Proust, "as surgeons say, his love was no longer operable."

Only a single day after delivering the "no" of his note, Scott returned to the shop with the "yes" of his handshake and smile. He'd received and read the third installment of "How Scott Aaron Matthews Can Change Your Life" and had begun to understand there was more to my story line than he'd first guessed. When he appeared at the shop door, I said to him, "So. I guess the honeymoon is over."

And we both laughed with the irrepressible joy of two children giggling in church, each knowing the other had gotten the joke exactly as intended. I no longer needed to speak in code. And as our laughter subsided, Scott said, "If only I'd waited one more day...."

But it was good that he'd not. There was perfection in what had at first seemed ill-timing, so that now we could together work out the steps of this intricate dance. I walked over to my book bag behind the shop counter and pulled out the note Scott had written, saying, "I'm going to keep this until I receive a retraction."

Scott's lips tightened, his head nodding in slow agreement. He then stuck out his hand to seal the deal with a succinct shake.

When he left the shop that morning I felt at ease with the world, more at peace, I think, than I'd felt since Patrick had begun his nightly blackouts. Now the air raid siren sounded the all clear. We'd crossed an inland sea, disappeared on the horizon, and come to a new world whose tarnished surface had been rubbed clean. The natives reflected thereon would no longer be misnamed to suit someone's error. And we'd not simply grown older in that world, we'd grown up.

Ed

P.S. The word, I have learned, is not *friendily*, but *friendlily*—which somehow doesn't roll off the tongue as easily. What a pity, nothing does.

October 7, 1998

Dear Nancy,

Still I remained in a certain turmoil. One day up, two days down. Three up, one down. Unknown to Scott till after the fact, our cockamamie honeymoon had been that brief stint leading up to the initiation of his reading group. By choosing Proust and naming Amy, a collusion took place, as though Scott were blindly following a Casanova's instruction manual to suave perfection. Defenses dismantled, I was vulnerable again. Bliss, yearning, laughter, beauty, sadness, and most notably an unquenchable aloneness I had nearly forgotten. Each of these I'd had with Scott, though the closest thing to physical intimacy we'd shared was a handshake.

The important unresolved question for me was not how long I could endure such a convoluted love (for what would be the option?), but how could I, Scott's friend with a twist, help resolve his unhappiness?

Scott was still in love with Amy. This I knew when I first heard him speak her name—even the moment before, when I'd observed his happy face like one half of the famed theatrical logo dissolve bitterly into its sad twin. Their engagement had lasted longer than many a marriage today, and her presence lingered in his life. But Scott was in busy pursuit of a replacement—"dating," as he put it, a euphemism for any number of activities. The trouble was, each prospective client found it difficult to live up to the original. No one ever can. No one ever should. What is needed is not a copy-cat replacement, but a second original, coming from its own place, desired for its own sake. Lookalikes only confuse.

Knowing this, and wanting to gain a better footing in Scott's extended family, I found myself eyeing the hand of each beautiful young woman I came in contact with to see if she wore a ring. Might this be Scott's bride-to-be and future mother to his children? Might I be so lucky as to find her and introduce them? More than once I thought to ask those with unadorned digits what they might be doing on a Saturday night—but always I backed down. Matchmaking is an antiquated profession, possibly the world's third oldest, and I was in enough trouble.

Among the prospective Mrs. Matthews was a young woman called Katharine. Scott said that Katharine and I were alike in our candor, and that their relationship was moving along a little faster than Scott would have preferred. For this I read "sex." But at whatever speed this particular love boat sailed, it seemed unlikely to find a permanent dock. Katharine was planning a move to San Francisco at year's end. Meanwhile she worked at an Italian restaurant, Siena, only a few doors down from the bookshop. Given this proximity, I wondered why we hadn't met. I speculated that Scott had mentioned me to Katharine, and that she'd disapproved of my behavior, that her sense of candor did not reach as far as my reaching out to her boyfriend.

One morning another envelope appeared at the shop door. Scott had again chosen to forego the P.O. and had slipped it through the same crack as before. Perhaps I should apply some gold leaf to the glass and label it "letters." On the envelope both my first and last names were printed, so that it would seem my love with a twist was gaining respectability. I hurriedly opened the envelope, pulled out the handwritten letter, and read:

"Dear Jane," it began. I laughed aloud, thinking what I was about to read was a parody of my own "Dear Nancy" letters. I wanted to ring up the Mister Quickie Printshop and when the receptionist answered, I would ask for Scott. As his voice came on the line, I'd muster a falsetto and squeak unconvincingly, "Hello, this is Jane. Is that you, Tarzan? Let's get together and have a Boy."

Going along with the joke, Scott would ask, "How might we do that?"

"We'll think of something," I would reply. Thinking of something, of some way to secure our friendship, had become the major preoccupation of my life.

The parody confusion escalated as I read on. The letter concerned a wedding that had been held the weekend before at St. John of God, which is that church at the foot of South Hardwick whose architecture I'd knocked. The groom's name was Ed. In the course of the Friday evening rehearsal and the ceremony following the next day, Scott had fallen in love with a member of the wedding party. This was Jane—and gone, I momentarily thought, was my chance at discovering Mrs. Matthews.

But the plot was to thicken.

When Scott and Jane were introduced, Scott looked down at her hand and stared forlornly at the engagement ring Jane was wearing. She stared intently back at him, bent near, and whispered into his ear, "If I weren't already getting married, you would be what I am looking for."

For each of them the meeting was something on the order of love at first sight.

They'd spent much of the ensuing rehearsal time together, talked with ease, danced all the dances at the wedding, and held one another close. It was a courtship built at breakneck speed, Jane's swan song to singlehood, and like one of those Russian nesting dolls, a little toy wedding within a larger one. In the letter Scott quoted Lerner and Loewe, though he seemed to want to attribute the tune to Frank Sinatra: *he could have danced all night.* Again this only added to my confusion. Was I reading fact or fiction? Or was this along the lines of those nonfiction novels where truth and invention are so inbred the resulting offspring may be beautiful but possessed of a dim wit and sixth toe? I'd also played with some lyrics from *My Fair Lady* while recounting my stroll down the street with the absent address. Was Scott even aware that these two songs belonged to the same show? And since when do straight men lift lines from Broadway?

When they fall in love, of course. When they fall in love.

Later the same day, Scott phoned me at the bookshop to talk about his letter. This had been no mock wedding, as I'd imagined, but the real affair. St. John of God is actually the Catholic church Scott attends—and he seemed to think I'd known this all along.

"I haven't been prying into your life," I told him. "Honestly, Scott, I didn't even know you were Catholic."

"Sure, Ed," he said, the nonfiction novel slipping into breech position.

Jane, too, was very much the real thing, but however fair, no lady. Though halfway married and fully engaged, when Scott appeared she'd lapsed into predatory mode. The letter I'd read that morning, with its accompanying explanation I'd not well understood, was the passionate proclamation Scott had written to Jane, but had not the guts to send to one already betrothed—and so had delivered to me instead.

Here was the Rube Goldberg reborn with a vengeance! And while I, too, am no lady, this latest twist seemed only fair. Both serenade and correspondence were at my instigation, and I still lacked a pressing engagement. Yet this letter again began on the same hesitant note: "I can't find the words"—though with the opposite sex Scott quickly recovered his voice. Were Jane managing a bookshop, *Remembrance of Things Past* would likely rise to the top of its list.

But when the whole truth of this began to sink in, it made me sad—then even a little angry. Scott was sincerely attempting to talk Jane out of her engagement.

"Scott!" I again wanted to hurl my words at that indifferent moon, but ended by turning them inward. "You've been there already. Remember Amy? Her reluctance to commit. The endless engagement. The wedding day set, then suspended, reset, suspended again. I want you to be happy. My happiness, too, is dependent upon it. But now you're attempting to take up with a woman who's considering cheating on her husband even before the signature on the marriage license has dried—and *you're* egging *her* on. She's just as likely to dump you when the next better model comes along. And it always does if you don't take commitment seriously."

Lecture concluded, and giving these thoughts the once-over, I felt like a hypocrite having scolded those with hands caught in an Oval Office cookie jar. Not only were Scott's and Jane's motives in pursuing each other abundantly clear, belonging to the free enterprise of courtship—so was their advantage. These two could easily imbibe the aphrodisiac of their mutual attraction, even flaunt the heady results—and in a church...at a wedding...one of them engaged to an absent third. They didn't need the separate but equal services of Dignity, Integrity, Ready-or-Not-Here-I-Come, or whatever name the alternative goes by. And even if this wedding party would allow it, Scott and I could dance cheek to cheek till all the churches in Summit, Pennsylvania, were transformed into Buddhist temples, but Scott would still not feel even a fraction of the passion he'd felt for Jane in a single instant. And hadn't I fallen exactly as they had, "not with a bang," or even the hope of one, "but a whimper"?

At the same time, I knew the source of my anger, and it was not unreasonable. Scott thought nothing of speaking openly to me about his sexual partners, realized or potential. But I kept quiet about mine, pandering, as it were, to his irrational discomfort. In the very first letter I'd written to Scott, I'd mentioned a romance that had left me vulnerable to Proust, but he'd never bothered to ask about it.

Why?

It could be that once Scott understood the genuine nature of that letter, he'd decided the less known of it the better, that a romance along those lines did not count. But I can count the ways, and I believe each way counts.

I'd had an equivalent Amy. His name was Jeff. And I have not seen him in more than twenty-five years, though he is still a part of my life and the long memory of love. We met in Columbus, Ohio, and like many a person coming off adolescence, thought we'd reached the end of youth. Economically unstable, emotionally insecure, we nevertheless were trying to get our footing, and I never doubted the veracity of the love, only trembled with the anxiety that is love in its infancy.

The added trouble is that when two men meet and fall in love, it is unlikely either family is there to coax them on. Nobody says, "Isn't it wonderful these two human beings have found one another and are in love?" Their coupling takes on the private practice of an elopement carried out under apartheid. There is no engagement, no wedding or official sanction. Absent is the tacky cake, bridesmaids, and best man. No bouquet or garter is tossed to the accompanying party of friends and relations. The two are left alone to rise or flounder in a marriage of their own invention.

And only twenty-five short years ago the American Psychiatric Association still labeled homosexuality a mental illness. How do you tell your parents you are in love when doctors say that what you think of as love is instead an illness? You are first entirely robbed of the social face of love, then you are saddled with an illness in its place. And what is the cure? Or, having been cured, what would be the result—*never to love at all*? No profession could ever have been so misguidedly cruel in its twisted diagnosis.

Through a series of accidents Jeff and I came apart, though I fought hard at keeping us together. We ended on opposite coasts, he in San Francisco, I in Philadelphia. For the whole of two years after we parted, hardly a day went by that I did not plot and dream of some way to bring us back together. But it never happened. Finally I began to teach myself to let go and get on with a new life. It took the passage of more than two decades and the most devious accident of all—the intervention of Scott—to bring the memory of Jeff back and to remind me of how I would have liked to have spent the rest of my life with him.

So when I see heterosexuals flouting the institution of marriage, taking it and their partners for granted, I get a little angry—sometimes a lot angry. The words of the ceremony have come to be treated like the fine print of a warranty no one ever bothers to read. And, it is assumed, if the contraption should malfunction, you can always get another.

But consider for a moment what it might be like if you could not even tell your mother and father that you had fallen in love. Never mind the greater institution of marriage and the family that is to follow. To be entirely deprived of that little pleasure, to tell Mom, to tell Dad, that now you are in the same special place they'd found themselves years before, and that the linkages of love go on even as they grow older. You would take nothing of the love process for granted. You'd settle for a plainer Jane who would not begin by thinking of cheating. And you would receive each orgasm as though it were the closest thing to "I do" as you would ever hope to hear.

Cheating, non-commitment, divorce—even blow jobs in the White House. These seem to be the order of the day. And in light of all this my love for Scott grows less and less absurd, begins to rise weightlessly with the suns and moons of my "star report." I hadn't asked for any of the above. I only hoped we could clear a small space where we could put a friendship and keep it safe from the added burden of its difficulty. There would be no document to hold us to it, no pomp and ceremony, no night of passion to revisit in memory years later.

But passion there could be. *Passion there is.* We could be friends, free to come and go as friends do. But there would be this one thing more, an understanding that the bittersweet twist was neither a bad omen nor a sad turn, but a bridge. We could talk openly, share books, delight in music, dish the mall mentality, and wonder just why it is that Titanic became the highest-grossing motion picture of all time. And why couldn't we, in our own small way, pull off a similar coup?

This friendship, too, could find its space in the long memory of love.

Ed

How Scott Aaron Matthews Can Change Your Life, Part Ten

To the long memory of Matthew Shepard
—born December 1, 1976; died October 12, 1998—
and the short memory of hate

In October 1998, Matthew Shepard, a gay University of Wyoming student, was entrapped by two young men, Russell Henderson and Aaron McKinney. Shepard was then tied to a buck fence, savagely beaten, and left alone to die.

October 12, 1998

Dear Nancy,

On Friday, after my legitimate hike to Olde Money Savings and Loan, I once again turned up South Hardwick Avenue, my goal to hand-deliver a brief note to Scott. Though hardly our nuptials, the writing keeps me connected, bringing purpose, even, to an apparently purposeless love.

The day was crisp, bright, an Alice-blue sky, filling me with the peaceful exhilaration I associate with childhood and the final day of school before a long vacation. A low-flying flock of southbound Canada geese forming a perfect wedge honked above my head. As if to complete this harmonic convergence, I revived the habit of a lifetime and paused at the railway trestle to read the graffiti there. What is an eyesore for some begins another story for me. And though this wayward poetry is often spoken in anger and a four-letter word, that anger, I believe, is more rightly a cry for help. Trouble is, I'm never sure how a person really helps another, and will only suggest the premise of one profession might be applied to all: first, do no harm.

But about all I knew on this day was that I hadn't come to South Hardwick to ask that Scott return my love. To have gotten beyond that temporary blackout and not be sent down again was enough. To be the recipient of unsweetened cups of coffee and a love letter meant for another said more than enough. And while these may amount to crumbs, they ought to remind us that something insignificant as tea and madeleine cake can conjure a world when served up at the right moment.

Scott was my madeleine.

So this day the jet stream pumped northerly air to my table and I could breathe freely, cast a sigh to that trickster, fate, then pause to read the graffiti.

It says:

NOW ENTERING LITTLE MIAMI 4-EVER

The words crowd the space like an unplanned pregnancy pressing at the womb, and I wondered how often people pass beneath them without taking notice.

But what does it all mean?

And aren't we a silly folk who find meaning not only in "stop" and "go" signs, but in which way the silver points when it drops to the floor, or the crack you sidestep in the pavement? But we're like that. I've spent years talking myself out of it, but we are just like that.

Early each autumn, about the first frost, I spy a praying mantis clinging to the shop window. Greeting him, I ask why he has come—to pray for another meal, or the mercy of a brief winter? I catch people in the same pose, throwing prayers at problems in hope that problems go away. The problems do not go away, only shift residences, visiting each in turn.

Leaning closer, I ask my annual guest, "May I interest you in a field guide to spiders?" He cocks his head, perhaps to suggest his taste leans toward six legs, but I've yet to hear a plain answer. It could be this he-mantis is a propositioning she. Though I lack good sense when it comes to sexual orientation, I do know better than to get chummy with a female mantis.

But since I find myself annually addressing an insect who's yet to answer, I may as well get on with the questions I ask myself.

What does it mean?

LITTLE MIAMI? Sounds like the downsized hope of a Paris, Texas. 4-EVER? No more than a Peter Pan promise without parole. Had I read this on my original visit, the meaning I'd have taken is:

KEEP OUT!

But as a veteran what I'm hearing is:

WELCOME!

So there we are. Meanings flip like nickels tossed—sometimes heads, sometimes tails—but we think meaning is fixed, or else we fix it to suit our immediate need. And when the nickel tossed fails to shake out right, we go for two out of three.

But with this visit my thoughts had become so single-minded I might as well have put up my own graffiti, its message the short dose of a five-letter word:

SCOTT!

I can see from the corner of my eye that a certain mantis on the make has raised her brow, perhaps to propose a double date. Best to recall those words of Kipling about keeping your head while everyone else is losing theirs. Thus far I'd kept mine, and sticking to my guns with Scott, had neither backed down nor pulled the trigger. And, look, the air had cleared, the doubtful Tommies sent cowering as though shell-shocked. By overlooking that crumb in favor of a wedding cake Martha Stewart might've knocked together on a coffee break, they miss out on a world.

But surely those in attendance at St. John's would say I was heading up the wrong street, that I might even deserve the same fate as Matthew Shepard, strung up and left for dead. Nothing so merciful as sudden death there, more like the piecemeal penalty of being drawn and quartered. I am glad, at least, that Patrick didn't live to hear about it. He fell before Matthew Shepard, Mother Teresa, and Princess Di. Now there's a trio to get chummy with.

Passing beneath the railway trestle, I saw the atmosphere immediately change. What had been the ruckus of commercial before, was replaced by the peace and quiet of residential after. Pottersville if George Bailey hadn't been born, Bedford Falls because he had.

A man in a car passed me. His skin was dark. A garbage truck with a crew of three retrieved trash cans. The crew was integrated. Then, as if a time capsule sprouted where a speed bump had been, I remembered what my mother told me when

I first told her I was gay. "Oh," she said. "Guess I'm not surprised. But if you are that way, then you'll have to go somewheres else where people are that way, too."

She probably thought she was being helpful, but she, too, did not know how to help, had fallen victim to the social code of the day. She maintained there were a couple places homosexuals existed—then all the others they did not. She'd yet to don the 3-D glasses you get at the gimmicky cinema, allowing you to see through the camouflage. Back then it was painted on thick and sealed with a veneer of varnish yet to crack. These many coats said you were neither gay nor homosexual, but only "that way," like those signposts Alice encounters in Wonderland. They fail to point out a town with a name and industry to boast about, but shrug instead, their facile fingers indicating

"hither"

"yonder"

"that way."

Yield, and poof! Gone would be your immediate family and friends, the woman you'd marry, the children you would together parent. It was as if you'd turned up the crowded road to St. Ives—seven of this, seven of that—and then paused to realize you're the one man alone.

But wait. There may yet be a place for that solitary traveler bucking the crowd, the entrance found at the back of a wardrobe, its architecture inspired by the green high rise of Oz. And if you followed that yellow brick road to the City of Emeralds, there'd be no shortage of interior designers to spruce up the place.

Or it could turn out to be like that remote desert isle where everyone had their own set of Proust with all the good parts highlighted. And if you happened upon a stray footprint in the sand of this desert isle, you'd know straightaway it was a mistake. For here was a place where the tables were turned and Alice had cracked the veneer of her looking glass.

But when I told my mother about my proclivities, I'd no knowledge of Proust, alternate lifestyles, or even what it meant to be in love. Crushes come like rain to adolescents, and while I'd had sex, it was of the near-heartless variety—sex for sex's sake—which leaves you feeling about as satisfied after as before. So it was easy for my mother to pour salt into wounds born open and festering with the prejudice of the age. It was a punishment likely repeated in every household the announcement was made, its ghost haunting us to this day.

But thirty years have passed since then, the world a stage inevitably shifting. Keanu Reeves is now a movie star, indigenous people run casinos, and soon Oprah Winfrey will be able to buy the country outright, no mortgage.

And I had found a friend in Scott. Sure, there'd been difficulties. There would be others. We'd come to a bump in the road—that raised bit of asphalt and tar—but on only a single sun-drenched visit later, I am able to look it squarely in the eye and see this mound for the molehill it is. Slow up, Ed. Cool it. In a world transformed, Scott and I could together climb that speedbump like a pair of tuneful Von Trapps, chorus rising, the audience with us, too—and the Founding Fathers tucked away in the old folks home where they belong. Our friendship could prosper right along with the economy.

LITTLE MIAMI was a kinder place where the pot had melted and the kettle wasn't only black. A cozy, freestyle grid of streets, small houses, some not freestanding, but duplexes or triplexes. Call them rowhomes. More like you'd find in South Philly, not the suburbs. It wasn't what people aiming for the suburbs aimed for. But I took to them better than the grander houses found a few blocks away. There each brags of its presence and says if you have to ask, you can't afford to live here.

Then there it was, number 365 South Hardwick Avenue. Scott's house, a *home*, the simple frame tied to a neighbor with a shared picket fence, its gate open, wooden steps leading from the street. The house had been painted cream, but a dash of red, maybe purple, was folded into the mix, giving it a pinkish hue on the sunlit side and mauve where shadow fell.

In my hand was an envelope, a note within: "How Scott Aaron Matthews Can Change Your Life, Part Nine." I raced up the steps, a postman on a singular mission, and dropped the sealed envelope into Scott's mailbox. Affixed to its metal surface was a decal from one of the well-known nature groups: a bevy of beasts, both male and female mantises, climbing the plank of Noah's ark. I put my fingers to it, made a respectful nod, then turned to assess the view.

Before me lay a small suburban valley, yellow canopies created by sugar maples curving their way across the straight lines of houses. Autumn, sweet sweater-weather autumn, the smell of burning leaves—real or imagined?—filled the air. I felt triumphant as Scout Finch having outed Boo Radley at the climax of *To Kill a Mockingbird*. Her star turn on the Radley porch proved a moment of awakening, the point of view Proust had spoken of. The bogeyman haunting her short life revealed, he was made its quiet hero instead. I remembered, too, that Scout and Boo never saw one another again. He'd come out for that moment, performed the needed task, then returned to his reclusive self. Like Marcel putting out his candle, I put the thought out of my head. Replacing it were thoughts of Amy. How could she give up this solid suburban perch, its open gate, and the love of Scott? People throw so much away, as if each picnic were to be replenished by a loaves-and-fishes miracle. The real miracle comes when you learn to enjoy both fish and loaf as if they were the last.

Or it could be Amy's love for Scott had been of that acute but short-lived variety, a rich melody so soon appreciated that by a tenth hearing it becomes a monotonous ditty.

Who can say?

I recalled an argument from childhood where neither person would back off. As the war of words escalated to a shouting match, one of these Hatfields would say to the other McCoy, "Whatever you say, I'm a million times ahead of you."

As if this wouldn't have settled things, the other then said to the one, "Whatever you say, I'm two million times ahead of you." Such imagined leaps may serve opponents in a childish drama, but what of this moment on my journey? All I could recount was the outcome of two fellow travelers. Amy had gone her way. Scott his. And who was I between them but the smallest lick of glue that wouldn't hold a stamp in place?

I slowly descended the wooden steps.

Thirty years of change, remarkable change. Change so remarkable that in the space of two months a single friendship seems to have undone the custom of lifetimes.

But now comes this young man strung up to a Wyoming fence, his build so slight he'd been overlooked, mistaken for a scarecrow.

Matthew Shepard, the name gentle as a Biblical parable, reminds us how changing and remaining the same go on ceaselessly, that love can never be taken for granted, hate never entirely displaced. That coming out is not a simple step.

Scott would, of course, recoil from the unwonted advance of a gay man, but he's incapable of performing the dreadful act of Russell Henderson and Aaron McKinney in the murder of Matthew Shepard. He's more like the rest of us, tending furrows in a milquetoast majority. We don't know how to murder. We don't know how to help. Instead, we each cling to the window of our own business, look out for the local forecast, and not see very far or think about it too deeply.

But who's to say where holocausts begin? With death camps, or quiet vows of misguided loyalty? I cannot answer, will only suggest that loving wrongly has given me a perspective and daring I'd lacked before. They seem to ask, in the manner of a lawyer pleading his final argument to a jury, "How is it possible to love either the wrong man or woman?"

And times twelve the verdict returned is:

ONLY LOVE.

There's talk of the death sentence for Henderson and McKinney, the gut response to a heinous crime. But since life remains a terminal diagnosis, I fail to see the need. Rather, let them live, their public service a required course where each might teach us how such hate was taught to him. So together, in a great mutual heave-ho, we can find our way out. It is this thought of hate, and not any wrong-headed love, I'd like to see banned. Then we might all see fit to serve time in LITTLE MIAMI.

October 8, 1998

Dear Scott,

The business of love always goes on unfinished and so we might as well learn to live with it, as is.

Every now and then I think to myself: wouldn't it be nice if I were fifteen years younger and Scott were gay? Or: wouldn't it be nice if I could climb into Amy's skin and say "yes" to Scott? Or: wouldn't it be nice if Jeff had gone on saying "yes" to me? Or...? And by now you know where this is leading. Not to the proposition you once imagined and the "stop" I had to endure but refused to accept, but to the world exactly as it is and our friendship exactly as that is—which is doing remarkably well, given the circumstances and the odds.

The real world doesn't fade out in a curtain's close and a chorus of "Somewhere there's a place for us." This is the place for us, and it includes Amy and Scott and Katharine and Jeff and Ed and even that bitch, Jane. They are all there to love whenever you want them, if only you can learn how.

Sometimes when I am alone in my bed at night, I think that you are probably alone as well, and I see how we are really alone together. I turn over and kiss the cheek of my pillow. It is enough and a lot less messy. And then on another night I think perhaps he is sleeping with a woman tonight, and on one of these nights, in a passionate moment, he might whisper in her ear, "This one's for Ed."

She will laugh and say, "No way—he can have the next one."

And they will then both laugh and somersault to ecstasy and I will go on waiting my turn. This waiting, too, can be enough, and I don't have to worry if anyone remembered to bring the condoms. Though, by the way, I hope you did, even if the she in question is that bitch, Jane.

There is no room, no niche in my world for "Wouldn't it be nice?" What is already here is more than enough. And there is always a way if you can figure and wait and learn to teach yourself how to let go of the ache.

Let it go.

Ed

AUTHOR'S NOTE:
It is here my letters conclude. The story continues.

First they came for the socialists, and I did not speak out because I was not a socialist.

Then they came for the trade unionists, and I did not speak out because I was not a trade unionist.

Then they came for the Jews, and I did not speak out because I was not a Jew.

Then they came for me, and there was no one left to speak for me.

—Pastor Martin Niemöller

Part Two

To the memory of N. O'Brien and
Emmett, both the Lab I would often
pet and the husband I never met

THE SIGN ABOVE THE DOOR is simple:

> BOUND MATTERS
> JUST BOOKS

although I have long wanted to amend this and plant a post in the cement out front with a wooden finger pointing in every direction, each with its own label:

> Copenhagen, two thousand whatever miles
>
> San Francisco, three thousand two hundred whatever miles
>
> Blueberry, Wisconsin, one thousand five hundred three miles... and so forth.

I believe a town ordinance prevents such a sign—as small-town ordinances often do. Though with the change of seasons other changes come, towns and minds not staying small for long unless their intent is self-strangulation. I would add that many a life is lived precisely in this way: a slow death at its own hand. But by its nature the fact of a bookshop changes minds, opens and frees them. So each morning as I pass beneath the simple sign, put key to door and open it, I know that I do not know who will appear that day or from which direction she will come.

But always she comes. Even on the worst days in the Year of Our Lord of Icestorms—three in rapid succession, as bad things are said to happen—someone managed. Picture him on skates, a pick or ax in hand to hack his way. He is in deep need of a Lasser tax guide, his wife left behind but burdening him further with instructions to get some recommendations from "one of the boys," enough to see her through to the thaw. The shop itself doesn't sport a high-gloss polish, more the spit and low-grade shine of a family practice. It is like a holiday ornament remembered from childhood: slightly cracked though still of a piece. And dust. Why, even after dusting, the dust seems only to have been shifted around, a Peter and Paul exchange. No floor here ever sparkled like those Fred and Ginger floated across, the supple pair lubricated by the near-equal sparkle of an expensive champagne. At Bound Matters, couples generally arrive sober and in want of a beach read, an instruction manual, or something to augment the coffee table and impress friends. Or most frequently of all at this family practice: a well-put story that does not soften but engages the gray matter. And what prods these well-read dancers is not the too-many-violins school of movie music, but the local classical music station.

What is it there is about a bookshop? All the enigmas therein are not to be found under the headings—suspense, espionage, detective, whodunit. Beneath the simple sign out front could be put instead:

MYSTERIES WITHIN.

But that would only confuse those so easily taken in by signs. They would come looking for the red herring of a brand name only: Agatha Christie, Ellis Peters, Dick Francis. Nothing more.

Always I think there will come the day when organization will show. But it never happens. Organization, however, there is. What doesn't show on the surface is buried only a little below, though on occasion I have seen a neglected table begin to look like one of those charts measuring geologic periods—Cretaceous, Jurassic, Triassic. Thin bands representing millions of years, more time than we know what to do with and so we reduce it to a chart. And with the single swing of some lady's zealous handbag, I've watched those geologic piles tumble.

And that smell. What is it there is in a bookshop that distills that distinctive smell? Does it come from the collected bottom burps of poets Byron, Rumi, and Seamus Heaney, the scent rising unladylike from those fissures in the toppled piles? I think not. Rather it is the sweet blend of ink, paper pulp, and always the dust, the dust, that stuff to which it is rumored we are both coming and going.

What is it there is about a bookshop, especially a particular kind of bookshop? It is put into words about as easily as that other mystery: love. So in accordance with this story, it could be the sign above the door should read:

BOUND MATTERS
ONLY LOVE.

But again this might confuse, the mystery inside easily mistaken for one of those religious shops—exclusive, of the narrow, even pushy in its single-minded solicitation. My preference is the imagined sign I carry within. It points neither this way nor that, but is more like the multi-armed Shiva pointing every which way and dancing in a circle of fire. And were it not for a small town ordinance I might have my way. But I am kept in line, and so the sign above the door remains simple:

BOUND MATTERS
JUST BOOKS.

ON THE MORNING of Monday, October 19th, a sleek blue sports car with a black convertible top pulled up to the shop as I undid *The New York Times* from its wrapper. Out stepped Scott. Opening the shop door, I stared at the chrome hood ornament glistening with early light. Scott slammed his car door shut, and in the same fluid wave of his right hand pointed proudly, *voila*, to the vehicle. "I drive a Perzz," he said. "They say they call it that because of the way the engine sounds, but really it's just the name of the original manufacturer."

"Handsome," I said, watching a reflected cloud graze across the polished hood. "More likely that's what happens to some girl when you get her in the back seat."

Scott chuckled. In his left hand he held a white cardboard box, the familiar emblem of the Mister Quickie Printshop stamped on the white surface. Offering it to me as he walked through the open shop door, he coaxed, "Go ahead." Taking the box into my hands, I let the shop door close softly behind Scott as he prodded me further: "Open it."

Lifting the tight-fitting lid, I could feel the resistance as the rush of air filled the vacuum within. Inside were two copies of "How Scott Aaron Matthews Can Change Your Life." Scott had carefully reprinted my letters, binding each set in ringed plastic with a clear front cover and a dark back cover. Putting the white box down among the books crowding a table, I removed one of the ringed binders and held it up between us, the specter of my Gertrude Stein rising to meet Scott's Alice B. Toklas.

"It's like a real book," I said.

"All but the suggested retail," Scott went along with the thought.

"Point taken. Your bill, please."

"Bill?" Scott's voice lifted sweetly on a smile. "This is for you, your audience. It needs widening."

"Careful the wish you make," I quoted. "Wishes are children."

"There. You see? Very good."

"But of course. It's Stephen Sondheim. A line from *Into the Woods*. Patrick and I, we'd often listen to Stephen Sondheim. His favorite show was *Follies*."

"Sounds right." Scott's smile broadened, then deflated into a flat "Sorry."

"Don't be." I shook my head. "Patrick was always—he was the first to laugh at himself. Oh, sure. The drunk he became stuck me with a pile of bills, all unpaid. A temporary setback. But his real legacy? He showed me the humor in every situation."

Releasing his smile again, Scott said, "Probably would've had a good one on us."

"The perfect TV sitcom," I said, "with Patrick its perfect narrator. But I doubt..." My smile, too, flickered and fell. "I wouldn't have told Patrick about you."

Plastic binder in hand, I casually flipped the white pages. Though what I held amounted to a smidgen if placed next to the bulk of Proust, the weight of its tiny being seemed to increase with the baby's breath of the fan. My enthusiasm was stoked. "Imagine," I said, "straight guy reprints love letters from gay guy. Sounds like a tabloid headline and about as preposterous as having sex in a flying saucer with little green men. You can bet the farm it's never happened before."

Scott shook his head. As if to borrow and twist another line from Sondheim, he said, "Send in the little green ladies," adding, "I don't really think of those as love letters."

"Right. They're not your usual love letters." I flipped the pages in the other direction, stopped, flipped back, then repeatedly compared the same two pages. "Did you notice?" I asked. "My handwriting. It changed." As the pages turned again, the white flutter recalled words of the familiar Frost poem:

"The woods are lovely, dark, and deep...."

"See?" I halted at the transition, an internal promise to keep. "Before this page the writing is tiny, pointed. Beyond, the words become larger, rounder."

Scott stared at the *Dear Nancy* salutation. "I guess I hadn't noticed before. Why do it that way?"

"I didn't know I'd done it at all. I wrote those letters under such pressure. How could you understand? I wrote one, sent it. Wrote another, sent that. And since I wasn't keeping copies, I couldn't compare one letter to the next, only hoped I was making sense. Consider it from my point of view: *what a stunt I was trying to pull!*—to figure some way of propositioning you without propositioning you. A crack so slight not even light gets through. Where is it? I didn't know. But there...." I nodded at the handwritten text. "You can see it in the words. Here's where I slipped through that crack."

Scott looked at the transitional page. "That's the letter I got," he pointed to the date at the top, "the same day I left the note asking you to stop."

"Our letters crossed in the mails," I said. "Isn't that supposed to mean something?"

Scott frowned. "But you don't believe in those things. The world according to Ed is all happenstance. And I didn't bother with the mails, slipped my note through the crack in the door. I'm too cheap to waste a stamp on you."

"Too cheap for a stamp, maybe," I said, "but not too cheap to go to the time and expense of making these copies. You try so hard not to be a nice guy because you're afraid of leading me on. But the truth of it is: you are a nice guy." I said it as if I didn't believe it myself, considered my other possible fates, then added, "What I was putting out of my mind while I wrote those letters is what you might do in response—get out your gun?"

"Gun?" Scott reeled at the accusation. "I don't even have a gun."

"Didn't really think you did. But you might go out and buy one to celebrate the occasion."

Scott and I both laughed uneasily. "I can laugh about it now," I said, "but . . . well, fortunately I was right. For once, I trusted my feelings. I couldn't have fallen for a gun-toting homophobe."

"But I wish . . ." Scott halted, then stressed, "It is *my* preference that you'd not fallen."

"You don't mean that."

"I do so." Scott's voice rose. "Don't tell me what I mean."

"Then why didn't you destroy my letters?"

"I could never destroy . . ." Scott's voice disappeared into folds of confusion. He looked toward the shop door, then to my handwritten bestseller list at the counter, then back to me and asked, "Why don't you drop the whole thing? Quit the letters and forget about me."

"And why don't you forget about Amy?" I asked. "You called off the engagement more than two years ago."

"That's very different. How can you even compare the two? *Amy and I loved each other.*"

"Then why is it, " I returned the volley, "the two of you aren't together, yet we're still friends?"

"And what makes you so certain," the aim of Scott's words sharp as any gunfire, "that we are friends? This is a business. I'm a customer. You've inflated the whole thing."

I was taken aback. Silenced. And as this uncomfortable silence slowly lifted, I reminded myself of the letters I still held in hand, looked downward, and made a quiet offering of them to Scott. As if this were some new-fangled ethnic handshake in the making, Scott stretched out his right arm and rested his palm on the plastic cover.

"I'm sorry," he whispered his repeal, "I didn't mean that."

I nodded an *I know*, saying, "The anger is about forgetting. Doesn't come easy. Even now, when I reach my apartment in the evenings and open the door, I half expect to see Patrick in his chair. And I hope it will be the old Patrick, the one I could talk to." Picturing that tired orange chair, its upholstery pockmarked and stained, I asked, "And you know what?"

Scott mouthed a faint *can't*.

"Some evenings, I do talk to him. Used to think that meant you were crazy. Now I think it's talking to an empty chair that's keeping me from going crazy. That. And meeting you."

Scott lifted his hand from the plastic binder. "What is there?" He dropped his arm. "Why wouldn't you have told Patrick about me?"

"Oh. Might've mentioned this nondescript Scott and five sets of Proust. But had Patrick lived... my letters, the ones to Nancy, they'd have run out, stopped. When I met you... what could I? Nothing would have happened."

"But I don't get it," Scott said. "It's still likely I'd have found my way to this shop, would probably be reading Proust. Same eyes. Same shirts."

"But not me," I said, a flurry of orange chairs swimming in my head, choreography by Busby Berkeley. "How could I be the same? No one's emotional life is unlimited. His circle of real friends doesn't widen indefinitely. All by his lonesome, Patrick took a lot out of me. I did what I could to hold him up, to talk him into getting help without demanding it. And in that final confusing week it seemed I made a little progress."

"Progress," Scott said, incredulous. "How progress?"

"Patrick went cold turkey," I answered. "He quit alcohol after ten years of almost nothing but. For him to glimpse his life sober without a doctor's supervision—that must have been chilling.

But he made the effort. What I can't figure out is why—*why* would he have tried to dry out only to take his life just a few days later? He must have had this flash of insight: life had been wonderful before. Why couldn't it be wonderful again? But there was no way I could have known how bad things had gotten. So *many* secrets. The alcohol I took to be the primary problem—that was a symptom of far deeper problems."

"*Multum in parvo*," Scott said, his erudition showing. But seeing I did not understand, he translated: "Much in little. Tip of the iceberg."

"Tip of the iceberg," I agreed, continuing. "After the suicide, putting the pieces together, I realized that were it not for me, Patrick would likely have been dead long before. I imagine the feeling is like caring for an elderly parent who is suddenly gone. To know their suffering is over comes as a relief, but then this big hole opens up."

"Straight to China." Scott concluded my thought and asked, "Did Patrick like Proust?"

"No way," my head shook involuntarily. "When it came to fiction, Patrick was a *Tales of the City* kind of guy, loved *The Godfather* novels and Donna Tartt's *The Secret History*. He disliked all things French on principle and didn't understand my feelings for Proust in the least. And had I told Patrick about my feelings for you, he'd have laughed, then disapproved, like a doting dad disapproving of someone his daughter had taken up with. He would have said you were just another customer from the shop, not a friend. And your not being gay—well. I'd have kept it to myself.

"But with you any need for secrecy went away. I even referred to Jeff in that very first letter. Yet in the twenty years I knew Patrick, I never once alluded to Jeff. Funny." I felt the puzzle come into my face. "Until this moment I don't think I realized that. You didn't slip some sort of truth serum into one of those coffees, did you?"

"Not guilty," Scott said, looking puzzled, too. "I would think two gay guys could talk freely about those things."

"Sure, we did. It's easy to talk about lightweight affairs, and Patrick was loaded with funny stories about his exploits. But the real thing. That's another thing. With all I've learned about Patrick since his death, I see what a master he was at avoiding the real things. And he was a master at belittling them in others. Patrick was possessive. However you and I expressed our friendship, he would have seen it as a threat to him. He had this delightful personality he put on in public—like a mask at Halloween, but it was largely bluff, the ravings of a showman. In reality he didn't have a shred of genuine self-esteem."

For several quiet moments I thought about the time leading up to Patrick's death. Looking down again at the bound copy of letters I still held in hand, I returned it to its white box and went on.

"Six years before the suicide, friends and family performed an intervention. Confronting Patrick, we got him to go away for treatment of his alcoholism. It was then, while hospitalized, that he was diagnosed manic-depressive."

"Tough stuff," Scott said.

"Tough enough," I said, "when you know what you're dealing with. But no one told me. Not a word from anyone in the family. From a doctor or Patrick himself. Housemates all those years. But it didn't seem to matter. Like our friendship was worthless. Secrecy, I swear, is a disease all by itself."

"Love has no use for secrets," Scott reinforced the thought. "It's what you said in one of your letters to Nancy."

"Yeah?" I winced at my own words and shrugged. "Makes for good copy in a love letter. But the day-to-day stuff. I suppose there's always one secret left unturned. Or maybe it's just that Patrick no longer cared about me, only his addictions. He turned his back on everyone. Refused the medication offered him. Wouldn't speak to a therapist. He stayed sober for about a month from his release. Thanksgiving until just after Christmas. Among his holiday gifts to me that year, Patrick included a bottle of Scotch, the first alcohol to be brought into our apartment since he went away. 'Just because I have a problem,'

Patrick said, 'doesn't mean you shouldn't celebrate.' I refused to open the box it came in, but thanked him, saying I'd save it for a special occasion. I should have known better, should have gotten rid of that bottle. Patrick, of course, found his own occasion—New Year's, I think—and emptied the bottle in a single evening. After that his downward spiral was precipitous, ending—slam—on the pavement outside our building. I didn't learn about the diagnosis of manic depression until the day of the funeral. An autopsy said he was HIV-positive."

Scott listened in attentive silence.

"Patrick must have counted it all as something to be ashamed of—a sexually transmitted disease on top of a mental illness. Isn't it bad enough that something goes wrong without adding the stigmas? Patrick, we all knew, was alcoholic. No hiding that. Then he was labeled manic-depressive, too. And years before, he'd been threatened by a third so-called 'mental' disease, his sexuality. Granted, on this count the American Psychiatric Association had been begrudgingly talked out of their error. But you don't undo the damage done by belatedly rearranging the words of a contract. Someone as insecure as Patrick would always know what people were thinking—that guy over there is just plain sick."

Emotion stuck in my throat and I choked, the air in the room sucked dry. Scott moved closer, put his hand on my shoulder, and squeezed it gently. "Go on, Ed. What are friends for? Confide."

Smiling, I recalled our trinity and continued.

"I remember when Patrick was reading the *Tales of the City* books. From cover to cover, all six of them right in a row. Somewhere in the midst of this firestorm of reading, he—who knew I'd spent time in San Francisco—asked me why I'd not stayed. The way he put the question, it was almost like an accusation: why leave that gay paradise of San Francisco?"

"And what did you say?" Scott asked. "Why did you leave?"

"I think I said I didn't run into Mrs. Madrigal. Doors didn't magically open; 28 Barbary Lane—that's a fictional address.

"Pity," Scott said.

"Pity," I nodded in agreement. "You see, Jeff and I, we'd lived together for a year in Columbus, Ohio. I was content to stay. But Jeff, he found Ohio suffocating, had his heart set on San Francisco. I didn't understand the attraction, didn't know how gorgeous an American city could be. I hadn't even heard of the Castro district with its swelling gay population. But if that's what Jeff wanted, I was all for it. He moved there ahead of me to find a place. I stayed behind in Columbus and worked, saving as much money as I could. The plan was that I would join him there in a few months—which I did. But in the interim, there in that gay paradise of San Francisco, Jeff found someone else. For a short while we did live together again, but it wasn't the same. I was too much in love to revert to being a casual friend. And Jeff's new beau was ten years my senior and well-established. Tall and blond, he had the sallow good looks of a James Dean. I felt I didn't stand a chance."

"Boy loses boy," Scott said.

Boy loses boy. The refrain repeated in my head like the easy line from a top forty hit, and in counterpoint I said, "But by the time Patrick began asking me about San Francisco, *he was lost.* So caught up in those stories about that city, I swear he thought they were real.

"Halcyon days of Mary Ann Singleton. You board a plane in Ohio that carries you to San Francisco. You find the idyllic furnished apartment, interview for a single great job—and of course you get it, hardly a question asked. You befriend this large cast of colorful characters. Even the likes of rich and handsome Beauchamp Day tries to pick you up. All this happens in the space of twenty-five pages or less. In Proust someone would still be turning over in his bed. Patrick seemed to be wondering what the hell was the matter with me that it didn't happen in just that way."

The glow of Scott's smile returned. "You mean Beauchamp Day didn't try and pick you up?" The smile seemed to insist: I dare you *not* to love me.

And I smiled, too, sighed, and said, "No such luck. I think it was the guy with the lemon candles."

Scott and I both laughed. The kind of great rockinghorse laughter that for the moment makes every problem you ever thought you had go away.

"So it isn't easy?" Scott said as our laughter settled. "Not even in San Francisco?"

"Maybe especially in San Francisco. Everyone clamoring to be in the same place at the same time. And what did I have? Next to nothing. But I was also stumbling around the truth with Patrick. Anyone who loves a city loves San Francisco. It's a cliché. And I would love to have stayed. I was young, could take the risks and ride out the disappointments. But love turns everything around, and I loved Jeff. And I couldn't stay in the same city where Jeff was. And I never told Patrick about Jeff."

"But why?" Scott again questioned. "Such close friends."

"You know how it is—different friends fill different needs. But in some ways you can't know. With Jeff so much was left unresolved." A lesser memory intruded upon the heavier stuff. "We still have an atticful of once-shared Fiesta Ware and McCoy Cookie Jars somewhere in Ohio." The quaint memory quickly vanished. "Just as when two men meet and fall in love there's no sanction, so when they break up there's no divorce. None of the mourning steps of separation is in place. One minute I believed Jeff and I would be together for life. The next it was over. Done. Kaput. You went through something like that with Amy. But though the love is the same, the trappings are different. You and Amy had options, supports, parted as friends. There I was in a strange city, my one anchor gone. And I don't think I ever came to terms with the fact that Jeff stopped loving me. It's the hardest thing. Better that a friend dies than that he goes on living but stops loving you."

"And why do you think it is, " Scott asked, "that you told me all at once?"

I shrugged. "Your timing was right. While Patrick lived, he became a burden, but only because he was so sick. He couldn't find a way out, slipped deeper and deeper. But he never ceased being my friend. He even tried to get well in that last week—did it more for me, I think, than for himself. But when he saw how long the road back might be, he just gave up. The End. Credits roll. My name is up there somewhere."

"Above the title," Scott kindly added, then asked with a start, "Why would anyone commit suicide? Life—it's so wonderful, Ed."

I looked into his eyes. The thought was foreign to me, almost a revelation: imagine never having considered suicide. But it only added to Scott's charisma, and I said, "For more than a year I feel nothing. Then you come along and offer me your hand. I'm taken in by your eyes, your smile, your sweet manner. I swear I prefer you in the simplest white shirt above the likes of anyone else outside of his. You bring me coffee and ask about Proust, lingering longer each morning in the shop. You offer to do a calendar to help out the business. You see a need, you fill it, don't wait until that calendar reads December 25th. But now you want to wish it away. Why? All the ghastly things going on in the world each day that you are able to live with, to comfortably ignore—then love makes you uncomfortable. That makes no sense to me.

"And to top it off, you shared your pain. Men don't often do that, gay or straight. Pain they hide. They put their hands on their Bibles, swear it is the truth they're about to tell, then tell everything but. Even Presidents are doing it.

"But not Scott. And with all those memories you'd stirred, without knowing it you touched Jeff. Had you marched into the shop and unbuttoned my fly, it would have meant far less. Ass you can get anywhere, but you touched the real privates."

Scott blushed, pushing his winsome face toward the floor. I wanted to hug him, to plead that he remain my friend. But I, too, held back.

"I don't know why I opened so easily to you," I went on. "But this summer I must have gone a little off my head. It was as though you were my oldest friend in the world, then—ooops!—one day I get a hard-on."

Scott blushed again and said, "It's not so easy for me to open up. It takes time, a long time for me to trust."

"But time—she runs out," I said. "And what about Jane? No trouble there."

"Maybe that was your influence."

"No way. Or haven't you heard? I maintain the highest standards, draw the line at engaged women and married men. So I wish you'd find yourself a non-engaged woman and—quick—marry her. Maybe I'm the one who needs to be getting out the shotgun."

Scott laughed. "But you didn't see Jane. A beautiful woman. You might have fallen, too. And really it was she who came on to me."

"You're a popular fellow right now. But don't blow it. It doesn't last."

Scott beamed. "It was exactly as you wrote about it. Doesn't take a second. But the best thing about meeting Jane is that she's helped me to forget about Amy. More than two years since the broken engagement and I still think about her every day. But only last week, post-Jane, I went through one entire day, thirty-six hours—cold turkey!—without a single Amy thought." Scott saddened. "But there are still troubling times. I hear a song we danced to. Pass a bench where we sat." Scott cast a glance toward my bestseller list. "See handwriting closely resembling hers. How is it that it happens like that, in a second, then takes forever to forget?"

"There, Scott. You can find the words."

"But I don't find it easy to share them." Scott hardened. "And then those letters of yours began to arrive. When I saw the words printed on the back of the first envelope—"How Scott Aaron Matthews Can Change Your Life"—my heart leapt. It's Amy, I thought, writing to say she wants it all back: engagement, upcoming wedding, the works.

"Then I saw the return address, realized it wasn't Amy, but that guy, Ed, who seems to have stepped into Amy's words. Ed who'd sold me Proust from that bookshop with the reputation."

"I should give lessons," I said, "on how to acquire a reputation."

Scott grinned. "But look what I did after I met Jane. I, a printer, who never handwrites anything aside from corrections on copy. I scribble out this passionate letter, then proceed to send it along to you."

"It's what I longed for."

"I hope you didn't think...?"

"No. Not for a moment. I was a little confused by it, opening a letter addressed to me that begins *Dear Jane*, but probably far less confused than you were when you opened my first *Dear Nancy* letter. I'd set a precedent. You followed. What do two men do in our situation? But let's get this straight and keep it there: I'm the one who's gay, not you. And I order you *not* to feel uncomfortable about the affection I feel for you. There's no need."

"But I do feel uncomfortable about it," Scott said. "I can't wish that away either."

"Scott, I'm asking very little of you. The same as before you knew. Your company now and then. No fuss over my need to write this out. That handshake. Maybe I can manage a hug out of you come Christmas. Anything more than that would make me feel uncomfortable, too. Don't you see?

"Oh, almost forgot." It was as though an unseen clock had sounded the hour. "Your being here this morning has saved me thirty-two cents." I walked over to my book bag behind the counter, retrieved a letter from it, retraced my steps, and placed yellow sheets directly into Scott's hands. Their lacking both envelope and stamp, I said, "Sorry. My Stamp Affixer is on the fritz."

Recognizing the allusion, Scott asked, "And what about your Ass Licker?"

"Right here at your service," I answered obligingly, then wistfully added, "in some other lifetime." Scott turned the yellow sheets over in his hands and a scowl darkened his face.

"But this isn't right," he complained. "Where's the envelope with all the stuff written on it?" Seeing it genuinely mattered to him, my joy sprang like a Grinch's heart breaking its seams, and rushing the season, I asked:

"How 'bout that Christmas hug right now?"

Scott and I embraced. He held me close as he'd held Jane, close as the thousand times he'd held Amy. And I remembered the last time Patrick and I embraced, less than forty-eight hours before his death, his frail body limp as Matthew Shepard's in my arms, Scott's now strong body up against mine. My next book: *A Brief History of the Hug*. This should not go on for too long.

And each of us sensing this in the other released one another as if on cue.

"Thank you," I said, the common courtesy falling flat. "I like your—what? *Tolerance* isn't word enough. Just accept my love. Know you make me happy. I only wish I could do the same for you."

Scott thrust my yellow sheets above his head. "You do all right by me," he said. "We'll be fine. Friends a long time."

Scott left the shop.

Even after his leaving, the sense of being home stayed with me. I took one of the bound copies of my letters from the white box and sat at my desk, reading them from the beginning, feeling my own story unfold within me. And then that sense of having come home, slumbering for so long, flooded over me. It was like the image in that Japanese print of Hokusai—a great blue wave of yeses washing up on shore, obliterating all the stray footprints in the sand. The plastic case holding the words is black on the back side, transparent on the front, the dark-ringed binder looping over the white sheets at the edges. Yin and yang, light pouring onto darkness, masculine and feminine rejoined like Siamese twins at the middle. All the mysteries of life contained within, waiting to be sorted. It's all there already, born complete with each awakening juncture. You need only learn how to read it.

IN THE WEEKS TO COME, I would show several friends the copies of the letters that Scott had made. Each of these friends was chosen by virtue of some expertise or point of view, but I wasn't looking for a critical response to my writer's craft. The letters, after all, had been born out of wedlock, a bastard creation forged in white heat and not sought by either their author or the recipient. They were indulgent, even gushing—but oh so necessary, and what I was looking for was reaction to their content. Had I been too soft on our President, too hard on a local printer? Was I deteriorating into a whiny, self-absorbed minority? Did I appear to be genuinely, if hopelessly, in love, merely infatuated, or possibly in the throes of a mid-life crisis? Had I given Patrick, poor Patrick, his due, or made a good description of the tooth-and-nail mourning process that shadows a suicide? Or was I plain crazy to have tried to pull off such an addled adolescent stunt?

Among these potential readers was Jerry. Both editor and writer, Jerry routinely immerses himself in Proust, is a champion of Broadway and Barbara Cook, and enjoys the intimate company of men—when he can get it. Only a single day after Scott had delivered the white box with its twice-told tale, Jerry arrived unexpectedly at the bookshop and I told him I'd written something I hoped he would read. He declined without query, telling me he makes it a habit never to read the work of friends, especially when he himself is engaged in a project.

"Outside influences," he said, dismissing my manuscript, "I keep them to a minimum."

So I told Jerry about the nature of my problem.

"That old warhorse?" he said in a tired pitch. "Surely there must be something more interesting for you to write about than having a crush on a straight man. Nobody wants to hear about it, and any self-respecting gay man would keep it to himself."

113

"I would probably have thought the same," I said. "But what I've written isn't exactly about that. That's only the catalyst. It's more about two people trying to behave maturely in an awkward situation, and about me coming to terms with my friend's suicide. Some of it's actually funny."

"Sounds a stitch." Jerry remained curt. "Your friend—what was his name?"

"Patrick."

"Patrick who drank himself to death. Yes?"

"No. Not exactly. He, uh, jumped. From the top of our apartment building."

"Gay man takes own life. Another warhorse. But please, Ed. You can spare me the gruesome details, though we can assume he was drunk at the time."

"I don't know."

"You don't know?"

"Don't know. Wasn't there. And those that found him—well, I don't suppose they bother to take a Breathalizer to a corpse. But I almost hope he was stinking, although I don't know where he would have gotten either the alcohol or the money to buy it with. He was in sorry shape."

"My dear," Jerry tipped his head, "dwell on this and you'll be the next casualty. Go somewhere sunny," he suggested. "You look tired."

"Tired?" I corrected. "I'm exhausted."

"Lighten up. See a show. Throw a party."

"You sound like Patrick quoting *Gypsy*. His solution to every problem involved some shindig or theatrical event, and always an accompanying pit stop for a toast along the way. That doesn't work for me anymore—and it never really worked for Patrick, either. Look at the outcome! And haven't you ever had a problem, Jerry, that you couldn't turn away from, no matter which way you turned?"

"My boy, I've had a few more years of practice than you, but I fail to see the correlation between theatre attendance and suicide. You discredit your kind. But don't think I'm oblivious as to how hard life can seem. I only regard it our primary business *not* to let ourselves get stuck in the hard places. And surely you know better than to get stuck on any man, especially one so obviously unavailable. I've always thought of you as more level-headed. So back up. How did this happen? Where did you meet? Who *is* he?"

"I'm calling him Scott. Scott Aaron Matthews. It's a composite name. Scott, in honor of that gay man, Scott Amedure, shot and killed by the straight man he admitted on television he had an eye for. Matthews for Matthew Shepard, and Aaron for Aaron McKinney, one of his killers. We met in the bookshop. He's reading Proust."

"Sounds exactly your type." Jerry made a fanciful face, batting his lashes. "I imagine him beautiful."

"I would say he's an attractive man. Women are drawn to him."

"Some men, too—but, of course, he's not married."

"Not yet. But he's very busy looking."

"And are you busy looking?"

"No. But you know how it goes. Sometimes it's when you're not looking that things sneak up behind you."

Jerry raised his brow. "So is that what happened? Did Scott sneak up behind you?"

I smiled. "Only metaphorically."

Jerry sighed. "That's all we're left with. But something beyond metaphors must have happened. You seem consumed."

"I suppose I am. But it's internal. Nothing much happened. I simply like Scott. And why not?"

"You're asking me?" Jerry posed. "Or yourself?"

"Scott was kind to me. Kind in the most ordinary ways."

"Kindness, I find, conceals more motives than cruelty. It's cruelty that's indifferent."

"But not Scott," I objected. "He's anything but indifferent. I wrote him these letters, you see. And he actually saved them, reprinted copies, and brought them back to me to look at. I might do something with them. That's why I'd like your opinion."

"Letters? How quaint. What sort of letters?"

"They're, uhh, sort of love letters. But not."

"Now, Ed. Be level with me. What would a 'sort of' love letter be? It either is, or it's not. Are you 'sort of' having sex on the sly as well? If this is a sample of your prose, it's damn sloppy."

"Scott and I could never have sex. Even if he were gay, I doubt we'd work on that intimate level. We're too different. Our backgrounds, our values, are different."

"Opposites attract."

"Opposites, perhaps. But oil and water? Scott's fifteen years my junior. He already owns a sporty car and a house in the suburbs. We came together simply because of some coincidences involving Proust."

"You came together over Proust? I see."

"No, Jerry. You don't see. Scott didn't have a clue what he was getting into. It was all an accident."

"So how is it you accidentally wrote him these 'sort of' love letters?"

"Actually, they weren't written to him. I only sent them to him."

"Do you possess a copy of *The Elements of Style*?" Jerry inquired. "If so, consult it. While you bluster emotion, it drains your clarity. Could be you should stick to bookselling, something you're good at. Leave the writing to authors."

"I might have," I said. "It's far easier. But I was pulled from my sleep. I began getting up in the middle of the night to make notes, strung those notes together over coffee in the morning, and sent them along to Scott. I didn't know where it was all coming from, but I had to go with it. And I was so afraid of losing his friendship, I overcompensated, fell overboard. The letters ran to over a hundred pages. I even suggested we might love one another, though in a different way."

Jerry snorted, then chimed in musically, "Come out, young lovers, wherever you are. Let *me* remind *you* that a different way is all you know."

"That's not true, Jerry. Just because you apparently know the scripts better than I doesn't mean you know all there is about me."

"That's correct," Jerry returned sharply. "You're a man of business, my literary advisor, not the light of *my* loins. When you were younger, cuter, I might have had other hopes. But look at you now. Tired and dragging, still mourning your dead friend—and now your business plan has expanded into the 'sort of' love-letter racket. I doubt you'd be interested in any of my comments. Try Hallmark. My advice, however, is that whatever is written in the middle of the night ought to be put off till morning." But then Jerry's stubbornness caved in to curiosity. "You've roused my wonder in one way. Why would a straight guy—*any guy*—reprint love letters written to him by a gay man? Something's not kosher."

Annoyance crept into my voice, and I said, "Scott's no dopey hunk, but a thoughtful man—ever heard of one? He's an...I don't know, there's an air about him. And he's my friend. Told me so."

"And did this confession take place," Jerry pumped me further, "before or after you began writing him these letters?"

"Before," I hedged. "*No.* After...but not quite. I wrote him one, you see, but he didn't realize what I was trying to tell him."

"Why am I not surprised?"

"So I had to write him another, then another. What began as a confession became a story unfolding."

"Oh, really? Recall what Truman Capote said about Jack Kerouac's automatic style, 'That's not writing, that's typing.'"

"I don't intend to end like either Capote or Kerouac. And I write in longhand."

"No one intends ending like either Capote or Kerouac. And how is it your story ends? Do you and Scott live happily ever after? Metaphorically speaking."

"My balls aren't crystal, Jerry. I don't *know* how the story ends. I only hope the friendship can go on. It's an interesting one."

"It would seem so. I think, dear Ed, that I will make an exception to my rule and read these letters of yours. I'm in the mood for a melodrama, and you have me intrigued."

The shop phone began to ring out just as the UPS man appeared at the door, several cartons in tow. He was followed by a stream of customers intent as picnic ants.

"I have the letters right here, Jerry." Picking up the phone, I spoke cheerfully into the mouthpiece. "Hello, Bound Matters." I paused to listen. "Yes, I think so. Let me check." Pushing the hold button, I returned the receiver to its place. Walking to my book bag, I pulled out a bound copy of my letters and handed it quickly to Jerry.

When he saw the ringed binder, he said, "Goodness. Does it come with a silk bookmark?"

"Scott likes to do things right," I said.

Jerry raised his brow again. "Quality act," he said, and then suggestively dangled a pinkie.

I hurried over to one of the shop's tables heaped high in apparent chaos, picked up two copies of one title and returned to the phone. "Yes, we have copies of *The Samurai's Garden*. Yes, Mrs. Pennyraker, I'll hold two for you. Yes, three o'clock tomorrow afternoon is fine. Yes, if you're held up at the dentist, three-thirty is also fine."

A voice whined from among the stacks: "Does this come in a paperback?"

Another was haughty: "The Manchester series on Churchill—is the third volume ready?"

"How late do you stay open?" completed the trilogy.

The UPS driver, anxious for my signature, was saying, "I've got an angry lady blocked in her Volvo." Letters under arm, Jerry motioned me he had to run. With phone still tucked between shoulder and cheek and two copies of *The Samurai's Garden* in hand, I awkwardly scribbled my signature for the UPS man. Jerry walked to the front of the shop, turned round at the door, and blew me a kiss. Seeing this, the UPS man turned and did the same.

I grinned wearily and spoke again into the receiver: "Yes, Mrs. Pennyraker"—and hung up the phone.

For all its noise and activity of only a moment before, the

shop suddenly emptied, turned quiet and contemplative, the alternate side of the same tossed coin. And just as quickly my internal questions expanded to fill the quiet. Had I made another mistake? Might Scott disapprove of my showing what I'd written to Jerry? Would Jerry get the wrong idea—*and what in Sam Hill was the right idea?* How would the story conclude? Staring into my book bag and seeing about a dozen legal pads jammed willy-nilly into it, I thought it could be my equipment was in need of updating. Time for me to graduate from yellow sheets and cheap ballpoint pens.

WHEN I WAS growing up in northern Wisconsin, my parents used to go for leisurely Sunday afternoon drives. I am thinking now of a time when umbrellas and telephones were uniformly black, neighborhoods strictly segregated, and color had not yet reached the blond chassis of our television sets. Of a time in my personal history when my loins had yet to be fully fired and a friendship could still be formed in a split second on the turf of a school playground. Of a place where the nearest movie theatre was fifteen miles away and was kept open for only three months of the year because the expense of heating it the other nine was too great.

Ahhh, but the family Chevrolet: she had been liberated. Gone was the black dogma, a hangover from the Model T that had lingered well into the 1940s. What replaced it was an integrated pink and gray—a favorite scheme of the day—and a climate-controlled operation the year round, an open window serving for air-conditioning in the warmer months. Into this machine would pile a second set of neighbors' parents—the Johnsons or the Larsens—one or more of their offspring, and me. As the 1950s moved into high gear, what had once been a crackerbox coupe would sprout ever-larger fins, and we would sail away, Sunday after Sunday, a double-dorsalled shark cutting along a blacktop stream.

The countryside through which we passed in summer was beautiful, but no more beautiful than our point of departure, a small dairy farm that sat on the gentle slope of a hillside I habitually climbed. Were you to join me in my climb and turn at the crest of that green slope, you would see to the right the tawny peak of the Copper Range and there before it the sharply cut valley holding the winding thread of the Brule River. Follow that thread and only a few miles ahead the Brule flows into mammoth Lake Superior. To the left of the scene, twenty miles as a crow would fly, rise the rocky hills of Lake Superior's chilly North Shore, upon which is built the city of Duluth, Minnesota. To the right, Lake Superior stretches steel-blue as far as the eye can see and disappears like a ghost on the horizon. This is where I began to gain consciousness—looking out, far as the eye can see, my imagination rising, then dipping, then soaring in the clear Wisconsin air.

Those Sunday afternoon drives were not pointless, but the destinations were far from grand. Often my parents would stop at a tavern for a cold beer. These taverns fascinated me, though at seven or eight years of age I'd not acquired a taste for beer—cold, lukewarm, or otherwise. But hung on these tavern walls were signs that pictured pretty, oval, blue lakes and wooded creeks that led to cascading waterfalls. These were lit from behind by some kind of strobe so that the water would appear to undulate in the manner of the real thing—which, of course, could be had by leaving that tavern and traveling for a mile in any direction. The purpose of those signs was to advertise beers whose names recall the sound effects of a Batman brawl: Blatz, Pabst, Schlitz, and so on. Strange and sturdy German names, so unlike the Scandinavian ones I was used to.

And encouraging this family affair, in and around those taverns various entertainments were put for squirts like me not ripe for beer. And I don't refer to the razzle-dazzle of electronic games, but the kind of thing people hatched when left to their own devices. One tavern, I remember, contained a bar not of oak, but rather a meandering snake of an aquarium stocked with tropical fish. Dreary locals would sit with their drink glass or beer bottle suspended above this abbreviated creek where colorful imports casually swam. Another place had a series of cages out back filled with exotic birds, some who'd speak when spoken to. Yet another had a playground with tire swings, monkey bars made of old pipe, and rippling slides hammered from sheet metal. But my favorite was this tavern that had a separate room crammed with boxed constructions that might have owed something to Rube Goldberg, had the proprietor ever heard of him. Each framed stage setting was glassed in and populated with small stuffed mammals, the real things, one-upping nature as she never intended. These were set in human situations. A taproom, say, in the Old West, a mining camp, or a lushly appointed opera house. And when you put a nickel into a slot (you could still do something with a nickel then), the scene would come to life. A skunk would start chugging ale, or a squirrel would open his mouth and out would pour an aria. A pair of critters would yank a saw across a fallen tree trunk. A door of an outhouse would swing open and a chipmunk would peer out, then pull the door shut again, outraged that he'd been caught in the middle of his business. This may all sound like a sorry substitute for Disney World, but it was more than an eyeful for an eight-year-old. Never mind the macabre nature of the setups, that these were dead animals whose lives had been snuffed in order that they be stuffed and made to perform before their said superiors, we human beings not content to love and leave things as they are. But squirts like you and me, we need our entertainments, and this may be far better than what will come later when we are ripe for beer and drop like drunks from the heights of apartment buildings. So what better use for our hard-won nickels?

Some days I think of the bookshop like that. It is very quiet. The heavy glass door with the crack has not opened in an hour. The phone doesn't ring. There are no sales, no deliveries, no customer demanding what isn't readily available. And then someone fishes around in his pocket, discovers a loose nickel, drops it into a slot, and the whole scene comes alive. One day the nickel brings Jerry. The next Sheila N. or Peggy C. On a hot afternoon the UPS man arrives in shorts and I see the shape of his legs and whether they are hairy or not. On an especially lucky day, the V.P. of a gas company, who has more nickels than he knows what to do with, arrives and leaves the shop with several shopping bags filled with books. And then one morning Scott happens along, and you come to learn about the interest earned on a single nickel well-invested.

It is my world. Or, at least, the part of this world I know best, though I also know it is a borrowed place, one that will not be mine for long. I can only hope that when I am snuffed like one of Marcel's candles, I will then be stuffed and asked next to perform for chipmunks, as they have done for me, and that they, too, will get their nickels' worth—as I hope you are getting yours.

But from what I can tell, we seldom have enough presence of mind to enjoy the Sunday afternoon ride on its first run. And when recycled and wrapped in the gauze of memory, the event may only come to seem better than it was. Too bad we can't negotiate the present path with tighter precision, to take curves at a speed that doesn't blur the passing scene. Too bad things get so confused you can't tell the people you're supposed to love from those you aren't. Too bad we are as we are, bound to an uncompromising clock. Stubborn. Short-sighted. Afraid to take, to give, however well your nickels accumulate.

So I think I'll hold to yellow sheets and cheap ballpoint pens jammed willy-nilly into my bag. Let those that need it bounce paragraphs around computer screens while I continue this love story at hand. It's not the sophistication of the apparatus that takes us to the place we long to be, but a plank leading inward to ground we all share. And that simple brush of pen to paper provides me with the brief illusion of being in touch with those I love.

A FEW DAYS PASSED AND I had heard nothing from Jerry. I don't know what hearing nothing means any more than I have the answer to that familiar Zen koan about the sound of one hand clapping. Since no one can solve that riddle, it gets handed down from one generation to the next, relegated like a once-fashionable antique or white elephant to the attic. Each age pauses to ponder its mystery, meditates on it a bit, then pops it back up to the attic, freshly dusted and undigested.

So here I am in the course of this unresolved story, listening for Jerry and wondering why I am hearing nothing. It could be the melodrama Jerry thought he was in the mood for is not the melodrama I'd written, and his silence is Jerry trying to figure out some way to break it to me gently. But Jerry has never struck me as the break-it-to-you-gently type. So it could be that Jerry has read it once and is now going over it a second time so as to pick up on the subtleties he'd missed on the first reading. Unlikely. Most likely of all, someone has dropped a nickel into the slot that drives Jerry's scene, leaving him with no time to read my story even once. We all have to learn to live in our independence with the many ways life puts us off—*and what is it making me so suddenly impatient with the process?*

Another day passed and the phone at the shop rang. It was Jerry having read what I'd written, and he suggested that we meet for lunch the following day to discuss my "manuscript." The restaurant he chose was Siena, one of his favorites, and the very place where Scott's friend Katharine works. I agreed with the choice but became oddly nervous at the prospect of meeting her there, as though this was not simply a lunch with Jerry, but some sort of perverse blind date.

The following afternoon I found myself awaiting Jerry at Siena's door. The temperature made a seasonable dip the night before, but had rebounded by the noon hour. Jacketless and without a companion, I became self-conscious standing outside the restaurant. I pictured Katharine within, face pressed to the wide window separating us. Her eyes were somehow concealed by the bold letters that spelled out

SIENA

thickly painted on the glass in colors of the Italian flag. Keeping my back to this imagined gaze, I rocked on my heels, nodding genially to familiar faces. For some reason, it didn't occur to me to secure a table, nor had I brought a book to read (a cardinal rule) in case Jerry were late. "Nice day," I heard myself saying to passersby. "Waiting for a friend." Increasingly I felt like that boy in a dream who gets all the way to school before realizing he's forgotten to dress.

Then Jerry appeared at a distance, a determined pedestrian on a mission. Cell phone pressed to ear, packet of letters tucked under arm, he waved at me before speaking into the mouthpiece. Advancing, he took his lips briefly from the cell phone and called out, "Hello, Ed." Returning to the other conversation, he signed off, began to thrust the gadget into his pocket, then retrieved it. "You really need one of these," he suggested. "Don't know how you get along. Been tied up all morning with my agent in New York who's been tied up all week with my publisher in Boston. Had you a cell phone, Ed, I could have at least called to say I was running late."

"You're here now," I said pointedly. "You can tell me in person."

"What should I expect," Jerry shrugged, dropping the phone into his pocket, "from the patron saint of the post office?" Taking the packet of letters from under his arm, he pointed to Siena's door, then led the way himself.

We were greeted by a pretty blonde hostess whose nametag informed me was not Katharine. I ignored the tag and dubbed her Amiable Amy instead, a nod to Scott's ex. She smiled a practiced saccharine smile and asked the familiar question, "Smoking or non?"

"Smoking," Jerry called out before I had a chance to state otherwise. We took our seats, and Jerry placed the copy of the bound letters on the table between us as he lit a narrow cigarette.

The restaurant is of plain decor, dowsed in earth tones with a straight double row of already-set tables and chairs running down the rectangular space toward the kitchen at the back. There, separating dining area from kitchen, a large, open-hearthed oven warms the entire setting.

A tall, striking waiter in white shirt, dark pants, and matching pitch-black hair and olive complexion brought us menus. Jerry dismissed them, as he had my manuscript before, and offered to order for the two of us from memory.

"Do you mind?" he asked.

"No. You come here often. You know best."

Jerry alternately sucked on his cigarette and sounded our order. As the waiter retreated with it to the kitchen, I stared noncommittally at his backside.

"Does he remind you of him?" Jerry asked.

"What?"

"Does the handsome waiter remind you of Scott?"

"He is very handsome—more handsome than Scott," I answered. "But no. Maybe a little. He carries that white shirt well, and he's male."

Jerry rolled his eyes. "As I feared. Utterly hopeless."

"You're an editor, Jerry. You've been published." I nodded at the black-and-white binder set between us. "What did you think about what I wrote? I probably should have done some revising before showing it to anyone. It was done so spontaneously. I should've at least changed some of the names to protect Scott."

"Does he need protection?" Jerry asked. "If so, maybe you could play his chaperon. Might save some time. How old did you say he is? And what of his appearance? You were vague about that."

"It was my intention to be vague about Scott's appearance, mentioning only a few details. Eye color. White shirts. That sort of thing. I wanted him neutral. Scott, the original reader, knows what he himself looks like, and I would like any other reader to invent his own Scott. His appearance is really unimportant for the purposes of my story. But to answer your question, I don't know exactly how old Scott is. I would say he's in his early thirties. He has one gray hair."

"You're keeping count?"

"It's above his right eye," I said.

"One of the blue ones," Jerry responded cynically. "You pick the oddest things to fixate on. As a reader I need to know: is he lean? Bearded or clean-shaven? Does he speak with a slight lisp? And why does he seem to be taking an interest in you? Do you have a photograph of Scott?"

"No. And I don't want one. Maybe when he marries, I'll get a wedding picture."

"Yes? Then you'll both be safe. In all the years I've known you, Ed, never have I once known you to be in love. I'm curious what it is that's so turned your head so. It's snapped clean off." Jerry pushed out the butt of his cigarette in a tiny glass ashtray.

"Jerry. I didn't come to chat about Scott. What did you think about what I had to say?"

"If you want my opinion about your ability, your style," Jerry answered, "I'll say this: there were times I couldn't put the thing down. And believe me, I'm not in the habit of reading handwritten manuscripts. It's nineteenth-century. Your word plays, too, can be interesting. But other times? I wanted nothing more than to give you a swift kick in the butt." Jerry lit a second cigarette.

The waiter brought out two wicker baskets, one larger, one smaller. He placed the smaller basket next to the plastic-ringed binder on the table before us. In its wicker mesh had been put a shiny cloth napkin with a colorful relief map of Italy printed on it. From the larger basket the waiter took two small loaves of warm garlic bread and laid them on the relief map. Tiny slabs of butter in a white ceramic dish were placed between us.

"Thank you," Jerry said, gleaming immodestly at the waiter as he moved away. Jerry then looked back to me, the gleam gone, and re-emphasized his former thought. "A swift *kick* in the butt. Your choice of friendship over sex is a cop-out."

"You know, I thought a gay man might say something like that," I said. "The problem is in the writing. It needs work. Those letters were written so quickly and I was confused by what I was experiencing. Confused and in a lot of pain."

"You were in a lot of lust," Jerry said. "The problem is *not* in the writing. You write well. Frankly, I was impressed. I had no idea you wrote at all."

"I didn't write those letters to impress. I wrote them to communicate."

"You wrote them to woo."

"Woo who? Scott? It isn't my place to be wooing Scott."

"And who do you think you're fooling? You're still being coy. What you communicated to me is how much you desire Scott. Now don't get me wrong, Ed. Friendship is a wonderful thing. But the reason I became so caught up in the reading has to do with the sexual tension, not your need for a pen pal. And I think you misread Scott. I think he's gay."

"Scott is not gay," I said, again not entirely surprised that Jerry had read it in that way. "The whole exercise was very wicked of me, even selfish. The sexual tension is genuine, but it is there largely because I sensed from the beginning that Scott isn't gay. Were he so, the tension would have been greatly diminished. There'd have been no need to write it out. I don't deny being drawn to Scott, but it's best to leave all sexual thoughts out of our friendship."

"Humph!," Jerry said, pausing to puff on his cigarette. "And just how do you know he isn't gay?"

"Know? You mean for sure. How can I—*how can anyone* know absolutely, positively about anyone? But since I never felt Scott would be attracted to me, why should it even matter? His sexual orientation is unimportant."

"So you concede he might be gay."

"No. Or only insofar as anyone might be." I paused, observing a smoke ring from Jerry's cigarette and thinking more seriously about the possibility. "But if it turns out now that Scott is gay, I don't think I'd much care for him."

"Nonsense." Jerry's voice rose. "Your whole story is about falling head-over-heels with this guy who quite possibly is gay, and now you say you wouldn't like him if he were."

The waiter had walked over to our table and was standing beside Jerry's chair with a pitcher of water in his hands. Ice cubes bobbed within, clinking softly.

"Water?" the waiter suggested.

Pour it over Jerry's head, I thought to say, but did not. Jerry nodded "yes," and each of our tumblers was filled in succession.

"Excuse me," I said to the waiter. "Do you know if Katharine is working today?"

"I don't. I'm new here and haven't met everyone yet. My first day, actually. But I can find out for you."

"Thank you," I said as he again backed away from our table.

"Are you sure that's wise?" Jerry asked. "This Katharine is Scott's girlfriend, right?"

"Yes, But it's not a long-term thing. She's leaving the area soon."

"Nevertheless, I doubt she'd have any interest in meeting you. Whether Scott is gay, straight, or middling."

I smiled. "I don't know that I've ever heard it put that way before. Middling wouldn't be so bad. But if Scott were gay pretending to be straight, I wouldn't like it. Would you?"

"I'll wait until I get a good look at that wedding picture before I answer that," Jerry said.

Now it was I who rolled my eyes. "And why," I said, "would anyone go to the trouble of being a closet homosexual in 1998? The Millennium approaches. They're even having sex in the White House."

"That wasn't supposed to get out," Jerry said.

"But it always does. The only difference between this time and all the others is that this time it got out while the man was still in office."

"He lied about it."

"A gut response, not that I recommend it. But people in far lesser positions have done the same. It's just fortunate for all those other Presidents that they never found themselves in a situation where they, too, would have probably lied about it."

"Whitewash," Jerry said. "You're changing the subject."

"Am not. Life is sex. How can you separate the two? With Scott I was trying hard not to lie about it while not provoking his discomfort at the same time, to show him how awkward it can be to be gay in a predominantly hetero world."

"It didn't work," Jerry said, emphasizing the point by putting out his cigarette in the now-crowded ashtray. "You failed. The awkwardness—we're used to that. But for Scott it was a new deal. By even hinting at sex, all you could make him feel was discomfort. He'd have liked to back off, to never see you again."

"Not," I insisted. "What he felt was confusion. For good reason. He thought I was about to proposition him. I wanted him to think that. Then he could honestly look at his own response."

"He can't do that," Jerry said, scraping a match on its wordless book so that it flared angrily between us. "And what's more, you can't make him."

"Make him what? Be honest? Why? He reprinted my letters. Doesn't that say something?"

"More whitewash." Jerry took a toke on a third cigarette. "He's courting your business."

"And I'm courting his. Makes the world go round."

"What does?" the question floated on a great puff of smoke. "Sex, money, or love?"

"Every one," I answered. "Every damned one of them."

Jerry flinched, but I persisted.

"Compassion. Conflicts, too. And probably a whole lot more I can only imagine."

Jerry responded with a resolute groan and said, "I've never heard of a more convoluted courtship."

"No? Maybe it's you, your whole way of thinking that's convoluted. Get over it. You can't narrow a life to a single relationship.

It'll die there. Like Patrick in his chair. But there's something I don't get, something about men. Maybe you can explain it."

"*Me*?" Jerry put down his cigarette, raised his water glass as if to propose a toast, then took a sip. Replacing the glass, he took up his cigarette again. "Why would you even listen to me? Your mind, it's made. Consult that sex guru, the one who writes the column. Or better," Jerry affected a thick accent, "try Dr. Ruth."

"Jerry, this is a conversation. I'm serious."

"I'm afraid you are. Far too serious for me."

"Look. Both you, a gay man," I pointed to the present party, then to an absent third, "and Scott, a straight man, seem to think that because I find him attractive, *his* sexual orientation has been called into question. When a woman expresses interest in me, I take it for what it is. If anything, I feel flattered, sexy, all the more loved. Heterosexuality doesn't threaten my orientation, doesn't make me feel uncomfortable. Yet this little minority makes this big majority nervous. What do they have to be nervous about? The species is hardly threatened. If anything, overpopulation is the threat. And it's not like every eligible male plans on running for President."

The handsome waiter returned to our table with two salads, a giant oregano grinder under his arm, and some news. "It turns out I am Katharine's replacement," he said. "Her last day was yesterday. She's moving to San Francisco. I'm sorry."

"Don't be, " Jerry said, first eyeing the oregano dispenser, then searching the ashtray for a spot to put out his half-smoked cigarette.

"Yes," I said, ignoring Jerry and convening with the waiter. "I knew Katharine was planning a move. I just didn't know it was this soon." The waiter turned to Jerry and offered him the oregano.

"Maybe later," he said. I declined as well, and the waiter retreated.

I crunched down on a bit of warm garlic bread, chewed on my thought for a few seconds, then said, "I was thinking about

San Francisco and the *Tales of the City* books the other day. That evening I got out my old copy of the Hitchcock film *Vertigo*, put it on, and let it play while I was eating my dinner. I remembered that it is set in San Francisco, but I'd completely forgotten that the James Stewart character is called Scott."

"You're obsessed," Jerry said.

"I didn't name the character. It was a coincidence."

"No accidents," Jerry reminded me.

"Who stands high enough to tell? No one I know. But the more interesting coincidence for me is with the Kim Novak character. I got out the movie book to be sure I wasn't hearing things. Her name is Madeleine, spelled exactly like the little cakes in the Overture to *Swann's Way*."

"You're magnificently obsessed."

"Jerry, I'm only looking at data. Observing phenomena. I didn't choose the names. I didn't write the script. And I'm sure glad I didn't. Fascinating though it may be, *Vertigo* doesn't make any sense. How did Hitch get away with it? And they call it his masterpiece. It says so in the movie book."

"And how do you suppose you got away with writing a hundred-page love letter to another man if he's not gay? Look that up in your movie book. You'll find it under turkey. No straight guy would put up with it, much less reprint copies. What did he charge you?"

"*Charge me?*" I questioned.

"For the service. He runs a printshop, not a charity. How much did he charge you?"

"Not a cent. He never even brought it up."

"The last gentleman." Jerry eyed me with suspicion. "So. This Scott reprinted your love letters at his own expense. He's reading Proust, likes to dress up, and is bringing you coffee. It's he who breaks off the engagement with his fiancée, though you're convinced he's still in love. *In love with who?* You know, Ed, I thought you were a pretty bright guy, but I'm beginning to think you're rather stupid."

"I may be, Jerry, but not in this regard. You haven't even met Scott, don't know him as I do."

"I can probably guess at him better than you, and I'd say you're proving as much a liar as our President."

The handsome waiter, anxious about the sounds of our rising voices, appeared with two pasta dishes, one in each arm. He put them quickly down between us and scurried back to the kitchen. A well-dressed couple, sitting a few tables away, watched the scene with some interest. Amiable Amy hovered nearer, smiling plastically through her teeth. "And how is everything here?" she asked.

Jerry and I turned to her and nodded simultaneously, then quickly resumed our dialogue as she floated to the next table. "Trust me on this one," I said in a lower tone. "I feel deeply about Scott. If he were gay, I'd know."

"Have it your way," Jerry seemed to concede. "But if it turns out Scott is straight, as you insist, then you can kiss the friendship goodbye. It's doomed. You and Scott will part enemies."

"Enemies?" I was dumbstruck. "How would you—why? Scott and I. We're friends."

"Friends?" Jerry twirled some pasta around a fork. "Check out the word in a dictionary. You hardly qualify as mutual clients." He dropped the fork back onto his plate. "Surely you possess a dictionary."

I made a meek nod.

"Then by all means," Jerry made another stab at his pasta, "*use it*. I can be very tough, Ed. It won't work. I have never seen it work. It always ends badly. It will go on ending badly." Jerry fell back in his chair and clamped his mouth shut, as though both meal and conversation had come to a premature end.

I felt I was being insulted, ridiculed, and that it was Jerry's and my friendship that was being called into question. All the work I'd put in with Scott, seeing the friendship survive the fire, redirecting my own sexual energy—and now I was being mocked by a gay colleague. Could Jerry be jealous because it seemed I'd pulled off something he regarded as impossible?

"Why can't it work?" I asked.

Jerry unclamped his jaw. "He is straight. You are gay. You think about him sexually. A straight man is repulsed by even the thought of having sex with another man."

"But I don't think about Scott sexually."

"Let the impeachment proceedings begin. That is a lie. You think about him all the time."

"I do think about Scott too much of the time, I admit—probably more than I should. But our interest is nonsexual. And how do you shut off love? Ask anyone who has ever found himself in love and he'll tell you it's impossible. It has to run its course."

"Your emphasis is misplaced," Jerry said. "Love isn't something you can measure. It's abstract. People use the word without having any idea what they're saying. But sex. Sex you can see."

I supped on a string of pasta. Maybe Jerry was right. Maybe I was being deceitful. What I thought would be a simple friendship with only a little twist—certainly a healthier stand-in for Patrick—was becoming an overly complicated nightmare, a Rube Goldberg gone haywire at every turn. All because of those stupid letters I'd written. When would I learn to keep my feelings to myself? And I'd not even written the letters directly to Scott, but to Nancy. It was more than just stupid, it was cowardly. Scott had inadvertently opened what was apparently my closet door, not his, and as soon as he glimpsed what might happen there, he'd close it, as he'd already once tried. Our friendship would end.

But, no. Twelve jurors rose in mutual complaint, their chairs overturning in the box. Jerry had slid backward, was sinking into the quicksand of Founding Father dribble. He still lives in a segregated world, and my friendship with Scott will hear none of that.

"You're wrong, Jerry," I shouted softly. "Isn't it equally stupid to say all straight men think and act alike as it is to say that all gay men think and act alike? What with Patrick's suicide, Scott's long, now-broken engagement, and all those Proustian twists, this situation is more complicated than usual. When I decided to embrace my love for Scott and write those letters, I gave up any thoughts about the sexual side of it. My interest is with Scott's happiness. Since my wanting Scott sexually doesn't make Scott happy, it's no sacrifice on my part to give up those thoughts. They don't belong to this friendship. Scott and I even joke about the sex. He's beginning to feel less uncomfortable about it. Only the other day..."

"But there. You see?" Jerry interrupted. "You do think about having sex with him."

"No. I think about *not* having sex with him."

"How in hell do you think about not having sex with someone?"

"I know it sounds strange, Jerry. But you can. You leave a space there. Whenever you come to that thought, you skip over it, let it go. You leave the sex part behind, and you hold tight to the love. Just because you've never experienced that doesn't mean it doesn't happen."

"Ed, you've simply lost it. Who do you think you are? *Sister Wendy Beckett*? That mystical stuff in those letters is plain crap. That's the weakest part. You can't get laid, and so not only do you go soft between the legs, you go all soggy in the head as well—drift off in the *spiritual* dimension. Nobody needs another book that takes that route."

Book? Had I said anything about writing a book?

"I happen to like Sister Wendy Beckett," I said. "In her own little way she has probably done as much for gay rights as any Pope ever will."

"More power to her. But you'll never make Pope, Ed. Not even nun. When you write about your attraction to Scott it's really sexy. I wanted to know: do these two guys get together? Don't throw that away, or you'll be left with nothing but mumbo jumbo. But if he is straight, then if I were you I would start forgetting about Scott right now. Unless there is something truly extraordinary about this friendship, it will come to an end—and with none of the drawing-room politeness of a

Noel Coward play. You'll see how ugly private lives can become when they're dragged into public."

"If I am writing a book," I said, "that's not the ending I want."

"If you are writing a piece of fiction, you can end it whatever way you please. You can roll in the grass with every rookie in Scotland Yard. But I wasn't talking about fiction, Ed. This is simple birds-and-bees stuff. *Wake up.* A gay man and a straight man just don't get it on—not when the gay man feels so passionately. It doesn't happen."

"I never did get that birds-and-bees stuff right," I said.

Jerry smiled and said in a calmer voice, "Maybe what you need is a refresher course. What are you doing on the weekend?"

"Maybe what I need is some aversion therapy."

"Whoa! That simply is not funny. It was all the rage when I was growing up. Lucky I got away with both testicles intact."

I cringed, picturing one of those musty museums, a shelf full of formaldehyde jars where bobbed the plucked and withering genitals of aged homosexuals.

As if to conclude the thought, Jerry chimed, "What's for dessert?" while I heard Amiable Amy ingratiating herself as yet another couple appeared at Siena's door:

"Smoking or non?"

From that lunch onward, I thought about how I could rewrite the letters I'd sent to Scott in a fictional form. I would change the names, rearrange the streets, make a beautiful church homely and a homely church beautiful—play God, if you will. Unlike my first letter to Scott, which had been unconsciously manipulated to spare his feelings by masking my own, I would now remove any question marks as to sexual orientation. The pea in this shell game would not be "Who's gay?" "Who's straight?" That would be spelled out in bell clarity and tucked neatly under the eiderdown throw of a novel, its beginnings something along the lines of

"Chapter One. I am born."

Then I would deliberately spin the casino's wheel, allowing that woebegone marble and accompanying chips to fall where they may. The Founding Fathers could declare the way—moat, crocodiles, maze of streets and all, with Summitt, Pennsylvania, taking on the psychological dimensions of a well-manicured theme park. The handsome barker at its helm would be Scott, who would point out St. John of God, Siena, and Bound Matters to anyone who could spare two bits for the privilege. And each fun-seeker would be chaperoned by a polite hostess who'd smile through perfect teeth. When asked, "What's for dessert?" she would reply, "Why, Jell-O, of course, three times a day," the cute wiggle of strawberry red repeated in the smack of her lipstick.

I have heard it said that when Patrick died, he went to peace—and who am I to argue the point? Whether death leads to another place, or those who fancy reincarnation have it right, or the end is abrupt and hard as that pavement where Patrick landed, his suffering in the course of this life ended there. And that is peace of a kind. But I believe that most of us—myself included—would prefer a small share in that peace before it becomes so absolute.

With Scott I may have found my way.

It was now the last week of October, those pristine amber days that annually unfold onto Halloween. I'd not seen nor heard from Scott since he'd delivered the reprints of my letters—and that was just as well. Like the rest of the eddies of our economy, bookselling, too, is a seasonal thing with the greatest push coming in the fall, leading up to Christmas. And what if Scott's holiday package had arrived early, been tightly wrapped, and labeled

"Do not open until...?"

The unveiling had not been premature, but long overdue. Now Scott's hug would keep me warm well into January, and Jerry's pessimism could do nothing to mar the forecast. And not only had my emotions gradually settled, but the dark cloud that had hung over me since Patrick's suicide had lifted. I could become a fulltime bookseller once more, put aside all thoughts of Scott and the rewriting until after the holiday rush. Then I would carefully weave in the subtle truths about love and sex, friendship and family that had been lost to me on my first harried attempt.

Among the autumn crush of new titles there arrived at the shop one morning a novel by Cathleen Schine called *The Evolution of Jane*.

How is it, you may ask, that even one more person would think to compose yet another work of fiction when there is only this single handful of very tired plots, not a new story to be found anywhere, merely old raisins cooking under the same sun? The vanity of all these dour grapes is enough to send a person permanently back to the worn family Bible. There the size of the print run, advertising budget, and the talk show circus is not the thing. Text and the faith of its reader are king. And in spite of its apparent appeal to the emotionally repressed and conservative among us, people in it do sleep around, do lop off

137

heads, do cheat and go on to lie about it—behave badly in a general sense. And the good do not always end well. In fact, they can end quite dismally. Figured into its many pages and multiple plots, the Bible also contains a disconcertingly high number of literal miracles. Not simply the power of love transforming lives, but water turned into wine, water into blood, and most dramatic of all, water parting upon request to allow the just to pass, then closing in on the unjust. And at one point someone turns into a salt lick only because she happens to take a peek in the wrong direction. The times were strict. But even given these supernatural leanings and special effects, the thing continues to have a contemporary ring and can be quite lyrical.

There is a drawback to this potency. I know only too well the drone and the dribble of those with their heads stuck firmly in their Bibles. Their compulsive readings can make a babbling drunk at the corner bar look like a handsome devil indeed, especially if you've had a couple of drinks yourself. So although water doesn't appear to be as flexible a fluid as it used to be, and there aren't any new stories to tell, there may yet be a new way of retelling an old story. Why not give that handsome devil a shot? Encourage any fellow who shakes up the familiar plot and shines up the old words. If you do not keep your vision keen, you may miss out on the resurrection at hand.

It was with this hope in heart that I smiled as I looked into a carton of new books and saw among them Cathleen Schine's novel, *The Evolution of Jane*. Here, perhaps, were the further exploits of that Jane who'd managed to do unto Scott what Scott had done unto me. Since otherwise engaged, she might be generous enough to give me some pointers—*and what had I just told myself about putting Scott out of my mind until after the holiday rush?*

I held a copy of *The Evolution of Jane* in hand. On the cover there is an Esther Williams type, her swim-suited back with plunging shoulderline to the audience. She sits on a rocky shore upon which an ocean wave is cresting, suspended. A dopey-faced seabird stands beside her, and a large, long-necked turtle eyes them both. Whether actual location or something of a metaphor, the place intended is the Galapagos Islands, that archipelago which set the Darwinian imagination turning and has now been a thorn in the side of several generations of fundamentalists.

As is my habit, I skipped the dust jacket synopsis, or blurb (an ugly, stunted word for something often written, I have been told, by someone who's not actually read the book), along with all those abbreviated reviews that may as well have been selected randomly from a dictionary and then hurled at the reader:

"Brilliant"
"Dazzling"
"Gripping."

Even the casual browser is threatened with exhaustion, made to think no book could be anything less than the work of a hyperactive genius. Once I would like to see instead:

"Lousy"
"Piddling"
"Dull and wimpy."

I would pick up such a book only to discover what went so wrong as to provoke honesty in advertising.

I turned to the first page of text and read:

"Have you ever lost a friend? It is the saddest and most baffling experience. No one sympathizes, unless the friend died, which in my case she did not."

I shut the book.

It was as though a disembodied hand had come out of nowhere, slapped my face, then disappeared. I was in no mood for such a tale—not from someone called Jane, or Jerry, or Jumping Jehosephat. Jerry's round-peg, square-hole prophecy had been depressing, and now here was this Jane person beginning her evolutionary tale with news of an extinction. The world according to these nay-sayers seems an archaic place to me, one I hoped to help revolutionize. But in most ways I do remain an archaic guy, relying on a handwritten text and a thirty-two-cent fare to communicate the fancies of my heart. Am I otherwise progressive or a romantic fool to think two adults can engage in a passionate friendship without having a mutual orgasm? If only I'd joined Scott's reading group when the opportunity had knocked. We'd have been stuck with one another for three-thousand, three-hundred pages. Not a marriage, perhaps, but an engagement on the scale of Scott and Amy, and with some novel variations on the ho-hum positions. I could have lain low through *Swann's* and *Guermantes Way*. When we got to those cities on that plain, I'd turn the session into a show-and-tell, jump naked from an enormous madeleine singing, "I did it my way." Sinatra might turn in his grave, but this would be a reading group that would get people talking.

I recorded the copies of *The Evolution of Jane* on the shop's invoice and surreptitiously shelved the bad news. This was not the time to talk of friendship's ending, but of friendship's deepening. Water may have edged no nearer to either blood or wine in my lifetime—*but what of it?* Both can be had in easy abundance without divine intervention. And it was official: Scottie had beamed me aboard. This counted as miracle enough in my book, and the purest evidence that life yet existed on this planet was to be found in my reprinted letters soon to be reworked for wider circulation.

That settled, and Jane in her place, I could look forward to a long morning of unpacking several more cartons of "riveting" though rehashed plots under the strict guidance of an eleventh commandment: thou shalt put Scott and this entire cast of characters out of my mind until after the holiday rush. As with some other similarly stuck moments in life, I must give myself that swift kick in the seat of my own pants—and get on with it.

It was later that same day in the shop, while shelving a book about the Hubble Telescope and recalling a dream of a few nights before, that I asked my co-worker Al a simple question: "Have you ever seen the Milky Way?"

I wasn't acting smart; I only knew Al had spent much of his life in Philadelphia, and that the Milky Way is invisible from even its cleanest suburb. In the dream remembered, I'd left my Philadelphia apartment after dark, walking through Schuylkill Park down to the river's bank. This river was far wider than the real thing, stretching like a great lake beyond the horizon. Then rising from the water itself was the Milky Way, its starry canopy slung overhead to the opposite Eastern horizon. Vanilla spray against black sky resembled the spewed come of a fecund giant. The dream tells no story; it is a single image painted by the mind with scraps of memory. But from even a single image a story can be built.

I recall how startled I had been some twenty years before when I'd spent two weeks one summer on Cape Cod and the first clear night looked up to the sky. There it was, the same spangled dome that had spread over me through the whole of my Wisconsin childhood. It was stuck in time, like Pompeii under Vesuvius' flow. Villas, bodies, loaves of bread in the oven and fishes on the table. Everything stilled, perfectly quiet, unchangeable, as though Darwin were wrong, the fundamentalists right. What I'd failed to see was how my child's-eye view had left both distance and time out of the quotient.

I'd no experience of missing the Milky Way. Other concerns had merely pointed my vision earthward. Having spent the previous years in various cities—Copenhagen, Columbus, San Francisco, now Philadelphia—I was slowly finding myself, while realizing at bottom how much the same each place is. And in those crowded metropolises, I'd simply forgotten the Milky Way. Or, rather, the memory had been misplaced, but never lost, like a diary penned under siege that anticipates liberation.

A starry night had been a given of my childhood, and had someone asked me now if I had seen the Milky Way, my answer would have been an assured but stale "yes." It could be we are all faulty listeners who, when asked direct questions, hear only ourselves answering but not the wonder in the question itself. Hearing "Milky Way," I would have pictured a grouping of lackluster stars too far away to count. But with my reintroduction on Cape Cod, I was the one silenced, stilled by a wondrous flow, while each star in that sky seemed to shout

"Yes."

"What have I ever done to deserve a night like this?" one of my companions asked herself aloud on that most perfect of nights. Breathing a collective sigh, everyone within earshot heard the place from where the question came and seemed to answer, *What, indeed?* Only the slightest ocean breeze licked at the face, like the tongue of a loving dog, and the lapping of water to shore was so even-tempered in its rhythm that Debussy might have set a melody to it. A curved row of unpretentious, white-shuttered houses stood too close to the waterfront and extended in a half-moon in either direction. And above it all was the toothy, broken smile of the Milky Way, that shattered rainbow robbed of color, then reset in pearl.

I did not imagine when I left northern Wisconsin that I would be leaving the stars. But all a Philadelphia sky will yield on the clearest of nights is the Big Dipper, Orion's Belt, and the glint of his sword, Northern Cross and Morning Star. Nothing approximating the density that so readily illuminates our insignificance and is aptly called the Milky Way. Any metropolitan area will dislodge the sight. City lights reflecting on lower atmospheric conditions alone can perform the trick, but where population rises, air pollution adds to the ceiling, draining the sky of its treasure.

So it was that Al's response to my autumnal question startled me.

"Yes," he answered. He had seen the Milky Way.

"Where?" I asked.

"In Philadelphia. You could still see it when I was a child."

In only twenty years, from the first point where Al might have consciously looked up at the night sky as a child, to the point where I first came to the City of Brotherly Love, most of the stars had been taken away. Twenty years. Only a twinkle in the life of any one of those stars. Given the rapidity by which fossil fuels have been depleted in this century (millions of years in the creating, a few decades of overconsumption in the using), it should come as no surprise. But the way in which time moves is the hardest thing for a mind to hold. A difficult day can sometimes drag into an endless night, whereas a decade can disappear overnight in the machinery of a demanding career. And whether day or decade or lifetime, when you come to the end of it—what is left?

Most of the stars are still there, of course, merely shrouded by our own collective being. And the light of some of those stars, traveling an incomprehensible distance, is still being shed, though the stars themselves have burnt to cinders. In the same spirit posed by my companion on Cape Cod, I cannot help but question such generosity, even to suggest we may be no more than starry-eyed onlookers in an indifferent universe. Yet it appears to be in the nature of creation that she remains generous, for there it is, the image lingers. Spewed come, shattered rainbow, pearly smile, each of us a matching constellation found somewhere beneath. Fumbling in and around and out of love, drawing up lists outdated before completion, turning down an unfamiliar street only to come upon a past long thought lost. Then, in near-equal proportion: letting go, forgiving, all the while trying hard not to take one moment for granted.

Once again, the day before Halloween, the pendulum swung to the far beyond, and I woke to uncontrolled sobbing. This time the outburst seemed to emanate from nowhere. I got up, went to the kitchen, splashed water onto my face, made toast, poured coffee. The sobbing only continued. I took a sip of the strong black liquid. Given my emotional state, I realized any caffeinated beverage was probably the worst thing for me. A shot of brandy might serve my immediate needs better, though it would constitute a dangerous precedent. In any case, none was at hand.

I took my coffee cup to the bathroom, poured the dark contents into the white bowl, and set the emptied cup atop the toilet. From the green sweatpants I'd slept in I pulled my limp cock and pissed directly into the heart of the black liquid: yin invading yang, yang invading yin until the arch of pale urine slowed to a trickle and I flushed the mess away. Cock still in hand, I looked up at myself in the mirror above the sink. My hair was disheveled, my eyes puffed and red. The reflected face seemed to dissolve.

I was sixteen, maybe seventeen years old and sobbing quietly into a pillow. I was in love, but could tell no one. No one. Not a trusted friend or teacher. Not my parents. Certainly not the person to whom my love was so obviously misdirected. There was no word for what I felt. True, I'd heard it spoken in hushed tones on two occasions, the time and place of each telling having stuck in my head the way people remember where they were when they heard that Kennedy had been shot. But when I went looking for that word in the school dictionaries, it wasn't there. "It" had been left out. Never mind the act itself or the depth of my feeling for one young man in particular. Not even the word had enough legitimacy to be in a dictionary.

I didn't exist. I was the space of an empty mirror, the unreflected race of undead, my one lover a pillow that held the mark of countless goodnight kisses. There was nothing worse than me, nothing less than me. Down, down, down. This rabbit hole would lead to a wonderless-land, perhaps straight to Hell itself. And coming to that place where the bottom had bottomed out, I met with Patrick's despair, a paleface rising up whiter than the whitest shirt, and as it did I landed

—SLAM—

on the hard pavement outside our apartment, just as Patrick had before me.

My own face returned to the bathroom mirror, and with it my sobbing abruptly ceased.

What had happened?

I pulled off my green sweatpants, turned on the shower, tested the water with my hand, and stepped in. The warm, rushing spray against my naked body was comforting. Not merely cleansing, but a healing salve enveloping the whole of my body. I was not the filth. The filth had come from somewhere else, and I'd carelessly gotten some on me, been caught in the nasty crossfire of a mucus-rich sneeze. Now it went whirlpooling down the shower's drain like the dark blood of a lost traveler in a Hitchcock film, the yin and yang of it spinning out of control. The chant repeated in my head: *I am not the filth. I am not the filth.*

When, only moments later, I stepped from the shower and began to dry myself, I didn't bother to dress at once, but went dripping naked to my book bag in my bedroom. I pulled a yellow pad and blue ballpoint from it and wrote in the hand of an automaton.

> I remember hearing that when Otto Frank and his family and friends were discovered in an attic in Amsterdam and were led away by Nazis to a concentration camp, the most famous Frank, Anne, who kept a diary, was actually pleased with the change. I don't know if this is true, or where I heard the story, but it seems vaguely credible—especially

for anyone who has read her diary and knows the spirit Anne embodied. The thought has always stayed with me: after more than two years shut up in an attic, might the open air of a concentration camp seem preferable? You cannot escape from that attic. Your purpose there is to remain hidden, safe within an invisibility, waiting for the danger outside to pass. But you can always dream of escaping in the naked, open air of a concentration camp. A guard may become careless, a gate may go unlocked. It all seems vaguely credible.

For weeks I have been trying to think up a suitable metaphor for the closet, one that might convey its deadness to those who have never known it. How do you describe a place that is itself purest metaphor, no compartment at all? No conscious person exists there, no true heterosexual has ever been there. And every homosexual who makes his getaway forgets the place as quickly as possible. Its memory has the staying power of a snake's shed skin.

The reason it is in my consciousness again has to do with the dual awakening that Scott Aaron Matthews managed to provoke in me, that beautiful light encroaching on that terrible dark.

What metaphor could bring the closet to the consciousness of those who've never known it or to those who think they've done a good turn by imposing it? How might they be made to understand that it bears no resemblance to the pain of unrequited love? What could possibly make a Nazi concentration camp look good, its air breathable? The metaphor came to me as I stepped naked from the shower this morning: it is Anne Frank's closet.

There is a world, and in that world there is a city called Amsterdam. And in that city there is a street. And on that street there is a building stripped of its contents. At the top of that empty building hidden behind a locked door there is an attic, and in the darkest corner of that attic there is a closet. And that closet has no lock. That closet needs no lock because it has no door. And from that doorless, lockless, lightless closet no love has ever escaped. And the danger of that invisibility may never pass.

I looked up from my yellow pad to the matching frame of yellow light that is my bedroom window, then back down to my yellow pad. I read what I'd just written, and it seemed so terrible I thought to destroy it, to let it sink to the bottom of another indifferent pile in yet another darkened room. I recalled the claim that some have made, that the Holocaust is a fiction of a Jewish-controlled press, and what Scott himself had answered when I asked him why he'd not destroyed my letters: "I could never destroy...." His answer had trailed off in conflict. He hadn't known exactly what he'd read in them that had warranted keeping any more than I had clearly understood why I was so driven to write them—why had I needed to discomfort Scott with such a ridiculous love?

I returned the legal pad and pen to their place.

Reaching the bookshop that morning, I put my key to the glass door, looked at the crack where Scott had slipped his envelopes, and felt my sobs return in full force.

I unlocked the door.

"What the hell is going on here?" I shouted aloud at *The New York Times* as I released it from its plastic tie. The slogan, "All the News That's Fit to Print" answered wearily from the front page. If those at *The New York Times* are so cocksure, why, then, doesn't the headline read:

> Straight Guy and Gay Guy Befriend
> Skeptics Are in Shock

I considered picking up the phone and dialing Scott so that he might reassure me of that headline, but reminded myself of the more recently acquired slogan: Keep Scott out of my mind until after the holiday rush.

My thoughts retreated to the two plastic binders containing my letters. One set I kept with me at all times, clinging to it the way Sebastian Flyte clung to his Aloysius. The other continued to circulate among friends. From Jerry it had gone to Audrey, who suggested Scott was shallow and that I should "be happy." From Audrey it moved to Michael, who'd found the story too sad. From Michael it moved to Pamela, who believed I had it in for straight men and stereotyped them. And from Pamela it had been passed to Betsy, who had the letters now.

Betsy I'd known for twenty years. First as a customer in the shop who'd gradually come to rely upon our recommendations. Then as a developing friend whom I'd watched make the transition from young bride to mother of one, then two. She'd pursued to completion several degrees in education and psychology and was now finding a niche working with "troubled youth." On her last visit to the shop she'd listened in bedside manner—intently, uncritically—while I replayed the sequence of events that had led me to the writing of the letters I now hoped she would read. And when I finished my story, Betsy had said, "I don't think it matters a tinker's damn whether Scott is gay or straight."

Though it would matter keenly to whoever was to become Mrs. Matthews and mother to Scott's children, Betsy had understood one thing instinctively. Like an unchecked virus amidst us, love has no respect for gender, socio-economic status, sexual orientation, or ethnicity. Transcending the lot, and hand-in-hand with eternity, it balks at proprietorship, its very survival dependent upon freedom.

Even before I bothered to snap on the shop lights, I went to the phone and dialed Betsy's home. I closed my eyes, anticipating a recorded message and harsh

"beeep."

But after only two short rings, my unspoken prayer was answered with a live voice.

"Betsy Eckerd," it sounded, the tone sharp, professional.

I was silent.

"Betsy Eckerd," it repeated.

"Yes. Hi," I stumbled. "It's Ed. Over at Bound Matters."

"You've a book for me?"

"Book?" I questioned, then remembering my place, said, "Of course. We always have a book for you. But that's not why I'm calling. My sobbing fits, they started again. I need to talk to someone."

"I have a few minutes," Betsy offered. "Talk to me."

"No," I answered with a jerk. "I mean, fine. But more than a few minutes. And not casually, not over the phone. I keep pushing Scott and this writing I need to do out of my mind until year's end. But each time I try to push it away, it pushes back at me. And every few hours this bleak feeling washes over me. Like I'm caught in a lava flow, can't move."

"Nice image," Betsy said supportively.

"Nice?" I growled. "Not when it's you who's stuck there. And this morning. I woke at dawn sobbing again. How can you explain that? Coming out of a sound sleep sobbing."

"My rule is," Betsy intoned, "don't be too quick to explain anything. But don't you think the sobbing has more to do with unresolved mourning over Patrick than it has to do with Scott? I was under the impression that things had settled between the two of you, that Scott's cool about the whole thing."

"He is," I said. "No one could have handled the situation better than he. No one could have been sweeter. Scott is not the problem. And Patrick is dead. The problem is me, other things, long ago."

"I see," Betsy drew out the words, hearing the wet panic in my voice. "I'm not sure I'm the one you should be talking with about this. It's really not my area. But I know a Dr. Hall..."

"Screw doctors." I interrupted. "They still can't fix a common cold. And I don't have a runny nose. I have..." I looked around the darkened shop, the heap of yesterday's arrivals waiting to be shelved, thousands more books, unread, already gathering dust on their shelves. "I've a friend," I said, "not a sickness. We're holding onto something, about to go over the edge. I need to talk—to talk to someone now."

Betsy remained silent for three beats, then said, "Why don't you come over to my office this afternoon around five o'clock? Martin has soccer practice then, and my husband is out of town on business. I have a couple of flexible hours and don't need to think about making a big dinner. But don't think of this as a professional visit. We'll talk as friends. Then you can decide what to do next. Though it's not specifically my field of interest, what you went through with Patrick, what you are going through with Scott, is very much my concern. And I have your letters here. I've read them, even made some notes. Much of what you wrote makes a good deal of sense to me. Scott must have thought so, too, or he would never have bothered to copy them. Keep reminding yourself of that. He triggered the poet in you. Hang onto that poet."

"Thank you!" I said with a vigor and more validation than was perhaps warranted.

"Don't thank me yet. I only hope you'll be okay until this afternoon. I'm looking forward to talking. It should be interesting, even fun. So take it easy. Read a good book. Cheer up."

"You sound like Jerry quoting Patrick quoting *Gypsy*."

"Who's Jerry?" Betsy asked.

"Jerry is—" I blurted, "It's not who Jerry is. But he thinks—" I threw my free hand into the air, gave it a dumb look, then withdrew the useless gesture and concluded, "Later."

As I approached the door of Betsy's office, it opened ahead of me and out came a lean teenaged boy with a severe haircut and a T-shirt that read across the nipples "Nine Inch Nails." A black leather jacket embroidered with metal studs hung from the boy's right shoulder, his tongue flicking like a serpent's to show off the trophy of a matching metal stud. I winced as we passed, the grand canyon of yet another generation gap opening between us.

The door of the office ajar, I saw Betsy inside sitting at a solid mahogany desk, studiously penning notes onto familiar yellow sheets. Her long, silver-touched hair was tied back, away from her pretty face upon which a pair of large, oval-framed glasses were propped in business demeanor. Overlooking her shoulder, and pushed up against the wall behind her, stood the slender frame of a grandfather clock. Images of suns and moons lit the upper slice of its round face, while venetian blinds sent a twin ladder of October light up a white wall.

"Next," I announced, my clenched hand rapping in accompaniment on the wooden door frame. "Sorry, I've nothing that's pierced—nothing I care to show you, anyway."

Betsy looked up from her yellow pad and laughed. "I think it's pretty weird. But, hey, we were pretty weird at that age, too."

"Not me," I said, passing beneath the gentle arch of the wooden frame and closing the door behind me. "I spent all my time reading, writing poems, and listening to Buffy Sainte-Marie records."

"You think that's normal for a teen?" Betsy protested. "The kids I see can't sit still long enough to read a page of text, much less to write a comprehensible sentence. I wouldn't venture a guess what they might think of poetry."

I shrugged as the grandfather clock chimed the hour. "It seemed to work for me. But I'm regressing now. All I do is read, listen to Buffy Sainte-Marie, and write letters to some guy who doesn't even much care for guys."

"You sound better than you did on the phone this morning."

"That sorrow thing, it comes and goes." And following the parallel, I questioned, "I wonder what there is about mourning that affects behavior in a way similar to your clients? When Patrick died, two things immediately went from me: my ability to read, and my need—desire, even—to write."

"How soon after the suicide did those abilities return?" Betsy asked.

"Reading, that returned in a matter of days," I answered. "But the writing. That didn't return until..."

"Until you met Scott." Betsy concluded my sentence.

"Yeah," I nodded slowly, trying to recall the pinprick in a haystack of memories.

"I don't believe there's any connection between my clients' troubles," Betsy went on, "and what a person undergoes during mourning. Two different areas. Many of the people I deal with have graphomotor problems or difficulty with phonemic awareness."

"Huh?" I mumbled, not knowing the lingo.

"Mourning, " Betsy's dialogue was textbook rigid, "is like a guarded walk on stepping stones. There's nothing more sudden than suicide. Were that not enough, issues of blame are right there, as though a murder has taken place. But who's to be charged with the crime? Victim and criminal are one. But unless shock triggers an episode of clinical depression, the inability to concentrate is temporary. It essentially takes care of itself." Relaxing her manner, Betsy pointed to a chair on the opposite side of her desk. "Sit down, Ed."

"If you don't mind, I think I'll browse a bit," I said, taking in the neat clutter of books and intellectual wares filling the room. "My turn to see what you're pushing." I spun like a dancer on his heel and asked, "Where's your couch?"

"Ready for a nap?"

"No, I mean..."

"I know what you mean. Couch is like a nun's habit. Optional today. And I'm not a strict Freudian."

"Didn't suppose you were," I said, my gypsy's glance settling on a ceramic figure of some goddess who held a snake in the palm of each of her hands. "Greedy, isn't she?"

Betsy's mouth curled a lazy crescent. "You don't like Freud, do you? In that opening letter you aligned him with fundamentalists, almost as though their two ways of thinking were interchangeable."

"The 'F' words," I said. "I'm no expert on either. But I respect Freud. Given the time he worked, I find his daring admirable. And I've never met a person—*not one*—who calls himself a fundamentalist. Either they all run in the opposite direction when they see me coming, or maybe there aren't any."

"They're out there," Betsy assured. "But if you admire Freud, yet haven't cozied up to any fundamentalist, exactly what were you objecting to in that first letter?"

"I was stressed out," I said, recalling my frenzied September walk. "Had taken a lunch break, but ate nothing. Returning to the shop, I was so drenched in sweat it was like I'd broken out in fever. That's it," I snapped to my own conclusion. "I was delirious when I wrote that letter."

"A pressured moment," Betsy suggested, "can prompt honesty."

"But was I honest?"

"Yes," Betsy insisted. "You did what you meant to do. You discovered a way to tell someone 'I love you' without provoking his discomfort. That's what makes the letter shine."

"But if Scott didn't get what he'd been told, then the letter failed."

"No, it succeeded perfectly, providing a good introduction to a friendship that might so easily have come apart, but hasn't. And no two people reading it will see it in exactly the same way. It holds your affection like a prism."

"Is that 'prism'?" I questioned, "or 'prison'?"

Ignoring my remark, Betsy said, "The problem is that Scott doesn't wholly inhabit his world. He's not fully conscious. Well, who is? You couldn't be the first man who's found him attractive. You're just the first to let him in on the secret. Men think nothing of making an unsolicited remark about a woman, almost as though it were their duty. Beautiful women grow resigned to it. Your method was far more interesting than a hoot or a whistle—and I'll let you in on a little secret: it gave me satisfaction to imagine this man Scott squirming for a time, especially knowing you'd no intention of laying a hand on him. But Ed, my question—you're avoiding it. What is there about Freud, about fundamentalists, you object to?"

The silence filling the room seemed first to increase, then diminish with the tick, tick, ticking of the grandfather clock. When I spoke again, it was in a measured pace. "Freud," I said, "Freud and fundamentalists. Don't both say 'there are no accidents'? But the—what should you call it? The Grand Puppeteer in each case would have to be different."

"Not sure I follow," Betsy said. "Go on."

"So where," I turned the question in on itself, "where's the difference? If there really are no accidents, no unplanned events, wouldn't that mean everything is scripted, predetermined? Our places would be fixed, like in a caste system."

"I'm not sure," Betsy said, "if the concept of 'there are no accidents' means that everything is fixed so much as it means that everything fits."

"But I don't think I believe that. I believe in the loose end, the piece that doesn't fit. The way you put it, even the disorder of mourning sounds so orderly."

"Shop talk," Betsy said. "You have to start somewhere. And with a troubled patient it's best to begin with a set of rules. Once you figure out where he fits within those precepts, you work from there."

"But what if he doesn't fit?" I asked. "I work in retail, deal daily with chaos."

On opposite walls hung a pair of framed posters, one a lush landscape announcing a Bonnard exhibit, opening and closing dates flanking the title; the other a painfully angled self-portrait of Frida Kahlo. "I imagine," I said, pointing alternately to the two pictures, "that's what it feels like to be manic-depressive. One minute you're a Bonnard landscape. The next you're Frida Kahlo being dragged along by a streetcar."

"A fair picture," Betsy said. "But change doesn't flick so rapid as that. Slow it down. Surely Patrick's moods didn't alter so quickly."

"He was my friend," I said. "We shared an apartment. It's not like I kept him under a microscope."

"But you noticed change."

"Yes. But not when we were alone together. Only when company came. Then everything about him became louder, larger, and increasingly vulgar. But I guess it wasn't the company so much as it was the alcohol. Soon as company came, Patrick offered them a drink. Even if the company said no, Patrick poured himself one. Out came Bubbles the Clown."

"Self-medication," Betsy said.

Annoyed, I said, "He liked to drink."

Clipping this, Betsy asked, "Why did Patrick take his life?"

"He was manic-depressive."

"Not an easy illness to diagnose," Betsy said. "How can you be sure?"

"I lived with him eighteen years."

"That doesn't qualify you to make a diagnosis."

"Then he was alcoholic—am I qualified to know that?"

Betsy inclined her head.

"I watched the drinking feed the manic-depression," I said, "or is it the other way round?"

"Hard to say," Betsy answered.

"And the drinking led to reckless sexual behavior, which led to HIV exposure, increased depression, more drinking, job loss, bankruptcy." I paused. "The breakdown of our friendship."

"Your friendship—it broke down?" Betsy questioned. "I thought you were friends until the end."

"I was there until the end. I've a problem walking out on people."

Betsy remained cautious. "I see."

"Do you?" My eyes narrowed. "Can you imagine Patrick's conflict? His lying so obvious. Collecting money from me to pay utility bills. All the while buying alcohol instead. Like a thief in his own home. It never occurred to me, but he'd turned off the ringer on the phone so creditors wouldn't bother him. Trouble is, no one else could reach him either. That left only me, nagging him to get help. And in the confusion of those last weeks—just when I thought I'd succeeded—without knowing it, I chose the date of Patrick's death."

Betsy pulled her glasses from her face, laid them on the desk, and leaned back in her chair. Pinching the corners of her eyes with thumb and forefinger, she asked, "How did you do that?"

"I had him sign an agreement," I answered, the October light slowly draining the room. "Made him promise he'd get help if I lent him ten dollars for a last bottle of booze. The day named became the same day he jumped. But I've come to think of this choice as his way of getting help. The means of dying, it was the only thing left him. That's where people mess up. Always needing to be in control."

Betsy nodded her agreement.

"Patrick had been drinking himself to death for years, but all he'd managed was a perpetual hangover. He thought of other ways. Once he told me about a trip to a gunshop where he'd actually considered buying a handgun. It sounded so out of character I didn't believe the story even as Patrick told it. Where do you go to buy a handgun? I wouldn't know where to start."

"The Yellow Pages," Betsy said. "It's easy enough. Too easy."

"Patrick told me that he went so far as to ask the clerk in the shop to take the gun out of the case so he could handle it. He'd put his finger on the trigger, pressed down, felt the resistance. But Patrick chickened on the deal. He left the shop empty-handed."

I stared into Frida Kahlo's eyes, the dark brows above them virtually a single road leading nowhere.

"But those last days. Patrick couldn't have bought a bullet, much less the gun to shoot it from. He'd not one cent in the bank, had driven his credit card debt up to thirty-five-thousand dollars. He was lucky to have gotten that last ten bucks out of me. But I gave it, putting hope in a handwritten agreement—my stupid yellow journalism. Nothing but a mounting pile of worthless junk."

"No," Betsy commanded, standing up abruptly, walking over to the opposite side of the desk to join me there. "Not worthless. That's your low self-esteem talking. Shut it out. In this case I know it's wrong. I've read your letters to Scott, to Nancy. And I think they have as much to do with Patrick—maybe more—than they have to do with Scott."

Betsy took my right hand and squeezed it between the twin cups of her palms.

"You right-handed?" she asked.

"Yes. The odds have it that way. Does it matter?"

"I don't believe so," Betsy said, releasing my hand. "Lots of theories about it, though, many of them foolish. When I was growing up in rural Michigan, a teacher I knew thought nothing of binding left-handers so they would learn to lead with their right. Imagine? Barely forty years ago. Barbarous."

Betsy walked back behind her desk and from a crowded shelf retrieved a worn copy of *Drama of the Gifted Child*, a book by Alice Miller. "Do you know this?" she asked.

"I've read it," I answered. "A good book."

"Eskimo snow," Betsy quipped, reshelving the book. Then reaching out, she flipped a silent switch on the wall. Beams of artificial light picked out objets d'art as Betsy resumed her seat.

"But Patrick," I said, pulling out the same chair Betsy had offered me earlier and sitting down. "I could never get him to read anything directly addressing his problems. He ran from psychiatry." I shrugged. "Can you blame him? By the last week of his life, Patrick's way out had come down to something cheap and sure as a jump from a high place. But as for the reason? I have a theory that sits at the very back of the bus, behind all the diagnoses of manic-depression and alcoholism. I think his suicide has more to do with his being gay than anything. He told me as much in those last weeks. He saw that he would probably never find happiness, and that my friendship was not enough to pull him through life."

"Statistics will back you up," Betsy said. "Many suggest that the gay male remains highest at risk for suicide of any group in the population."

"But don't you think that's changing?" I questioned. "That it has changed. Patrick's case was extreme. It's not like he was a gay Everyman. And attitudes have shifted. Look at the difference in visibility in, say, thirty years. Those suicide stats must be dropping along with that change. One morning when Scott was in the shop and we were talking about all this, I asked him if he remembered a time when gay people weren't around."

"And what did he say?"

"He said that as far back as he could remember, gay people had been there. He just hadn't known any until he began working in the printshop."

"Does that indicate change?"

I hesitated. "Yes. I can still remember when nobody used the word. I would say that indicates a major change."

"But Scott hadn't known any gay people until he was... what? Somewhere in his twenties?"

"I guess."

"Think about it, Ed. Scott is this outgoing, attractive, charming young man, yet he hadn't knowingly known any gay people until after he'd entered the work force. Never in junior high, high school, or college. And it's not until he's entering his fourth decade that he meets some guy who'd flirted with him openly enough so that he'd recognized what had happened. And Scott isn't especially unenlightened or unventuresome. He's reading Proust. But you practically had to bang him over the head with your—"

"Don't say it," I interrupted. "I can't even... I never...."

"My point, " Betsy continued, "is that he was slow to get it because he is so completely out of tune with the possibility. All those formative years in school there must have been one young man among the thousands who at the very least wanted to tell Scott, 'I think you're cute'—but not one ever dared. They all kept it to themselves.

"And then the two of you meet in the most innocent of circumstances. Two full-blown adults—Scott and Ed—but you were still crazy with fear that the moment Scott found out there was a hint of the erotic in your attraction the friendship would end. I would say this indicates that many of the changes in attitude you sense are real are more rightly only on the surface. And if you believe the changes are real, why would you suggest that it is Patrick's sexual orientation that was the leading factor in his suicide?"

"That's instinctive," I answered. "And it could be that as a gay man I'm so in tune with these issues—perhaps overly so—that I see it as an issue when it isn't. But Patrick did suggest it himself in that letter he never sent to his parents. And my having found that letter when I did, reading and keeping it, that was, well, another accident that might so easily not have happened. It's the only thing of Patrick's I ever took. The only thing that wasn't shared property that I essentially stole from him. I'll bet he would have destroyed that note right along with his pornography."

My speculation loosened another memory, and out came, "Accident or suicide?"

"What?" Betsy asked.

"Those few days immediately following Patrick's fall, the detectives couldn't decide what to put on the death certificate where it asks 'cause of death.' They kept leaning toward 'accidental fall,' and all of Patrick's immediate family rushed to back them up. Why didn't Patrick bother to lock the apartment door, they argued, unless he planned on returning? Why did he have his eyeglasses on? Why was he in stockinged feet? Slipped, must have slipped, I heard again and again. Oddly, their primary evidence was my own note signed by Patrick himself. He hadn't destroyed that. It was still tucked into the book he was reading that last week. 'Why,' the detectives had asked, 'would Patrick sign such an agreement promising he would get help if he only intended taking his own life?'"

"To get the ten dollars for the bottle of booze," Betsy responded.

"Of course," I agreed. "And maybe my counter-argument should have been, 'There are no accidents.'"

"So," Betsy smiled weakly, "here we are back where you started in that first letter to Scott—but with an about-face."

"Yeah. Maybe the thought should be changed to 'There are no accidental deaths, only suicides.' Kinda grim."

"But not so far from the mark, " Betsy said. "There are more suicides than you would know looking at that slot where it says 'cause of death.' Take your single firsthand experience of suicide with Scott." The last word froze in its place. "I mean, with Patrick." Betsy's face grew crimson. Burying the slip in a brief smile, she asked, "Patrick was your first experience?"

"Was," I complied.

"And what does it say on his death certificate," her tone hardened, "where it asks 'cause of death'?"

I felt like a student confronted with a surprise exam. A distant "beeep, beeep, beeep" pounded in my head, and when it wouldn't clear, a voice came from my mouth as if I were a dummy to an absent ventriloquist.

"*Suicide*," I blurted. "It says suicide."

Betsy was momentarily silent, then spoke quietly. "Had you not been there, it would likely have read 'accidental fall.' A lie would have been recorded. And although you will find other slots on that death certificate that ask for race, religion, and marital status, nowhere will you find a slot that asks for sexual orientation. Junior high, high school, college. An innocent meeting in a bookshop. Death. Even in death it remains under wraps.

"Change?" Betsy sadly questioned. "I think we still have a long way to go."

A last distant "beeep" faded in my head.

"So," Betsy went on questioning, "aside from what Patrick said to you in those last weeks, and what he wrote in his letter to his parents, what would you offer to the gentlemen of the jury to back up your claim that he committed suicide because he was homosexual?"

"Nothing solid," I said. "Nothing that would hold up in a court of law."

"Forget about the law," Betsy responded. "The law's been forgetting about homosexuals for too long. Your letters to Scott were spoken from the heart. Speak from the heart, Ed. You do well when you speak from the heart."

And so I spoke.

"Were Patrick heterosexual, it's just as likely he'd have been manic-depressive, and could've come to depend upon alcohol. He might've ended in the same way. But it's far less likely he would have become HIV-positive."

"Explain."

"Well, for one thing, a heterosexual in his forties—he'd probably be married with children. Family's a safety net. Not perfect. No family is. But something in a world of uncertainty."

Betsy quietly agreed.

"And if you could magically take the negatives out of being homosexual, then gay marriages, they'd just happen. Who'd bother to question their existence? Patrick would have been in a same-sex union. We'd probably both be. And I'll bet Patrick would have adopted. He loved kids."

Betsy smiled.

"And kids, they loved him. It would have all been there, holding him up." My head slumped between my shoulders, then rose at the crack of my next thought.

"But that's not the way it is."

Betsy's smile left her.

"It's like because you made one wrong choice, you're forever penalized. As if anybody—*gay or straight*—chooses who he falls in love with. It's not about choice, only acceptance. But gay marriage, that's the penultimate oxymoron, the sure sign Rome is about to fall. And when two men adopt, it's headline news, right up there with the latest political scandal.

"And what if Patrick happened to be heterosexual? He'd have stayed Catholic. The church would have been a safety net, too, not the noose it became."

The sums compounded in my head.

"So all these loose ends, having largely to do with sexual orientation, led painstakingly, almost inevitably, to Patrick's suicide."

"I would say," Betsy said, raising her hands from her desk and applauding softly, "that amounts to a very solid argument." She replaced her hands, palms downward, onto the wooden desk. They changed character, seemed to merge as a unit with the desk, the veins and ivory flesh of their backs swimming into the mahogany grain.

"And all my loose ends," I said, "from leaving Wisconsin to finding Patrick's premature suicide note and naming the day of his death. All led to that strangest of bedfellows. To Scott."

"Love at first sight," Betsy said.

I cocked my head and asked, "Did you ever read *Catch-22*?"

"Haven't."

"A lot of unconscious things happened when I did that writing. But it was a conscious choice I made when I looked into Scott's eyes and said I was like Yossarian in *Catch-22*. That love at first sight wasn't romantic. It wasn't sexual. I'm not really sure what it was. Maybe a literary device. When Joseph Heller wrote *Catch-22*, for a novel to open with one man professing love for another must have been startling."

"For some it still is," Betsy said.

"But *Catch-22*," I said, "it was written in the fifties, published in 1961. The reigning Pope would've seen that first line—and zap!—it would've gone directly onto that black list. Can I say black list?"

"In this office," Betsy said, "you can speak freely. But I need to be clear on this point. Are you suggesting you're neither romantically nor sexually attracted to Scott?"

"No. But it may have been my literary device to see if things had changed in the forty years since the writing of *Catch-22*. Of course I was bending all kinds of rules. This wasn't a work of fiction, and my primary reader was the man to whom the love at first sight was directed. My audience was a confined audience of one, and unlike Yossarian, there was a sexual component to my attraction." I interrupted my own story.

"But I need to back up. I said before I started writing again when I met Scott. Not so. Meeting Scott, that was like meeting anyone. First impression: attractive guy with an air of intelligence. No big deal. Maybe he supposed I knew he was heterosexual. Maybe straight men always do that, even when they're not cloaked with wife and child. But being gay, you see things differently. You know how twisted they can become. And even when I had that fleeting thought 'I wonder if Scott's gay?' I didn't think he'd be interested in me."

"Why not?" Betsy asked. "People like you. I like you."

"Sure. As a bookseller. Someone who's easy to deal with. But it takes more than a mutual interest in Proust to.... Well, I just figured, if Scott wanted a steady male partner, he'd have found one among his peers.

"But don't you see, Betsy? That was before. I began writing again only after I pointed to my list and Scott told me about Amy. What a relief, the guy's not gay. So my defenses dropped. Scott is heterosexual, and I don't come on to straight men. Why come on to anyone where your advance is unwanted?"

"But don't you see, Ed? A lot of men think it's expected of them."

"Not me," I winced. "But that's exactly where it happened."

"It?"

"Yeah. Sex exited, love happened. I don't think I'd ever felt that clean split before. Love and sex. Two distinct things. The feeling was new, was renewing. So fresh. Maybe the first breath of fresh air I'd taken since Patrick's death. I couldn't keep it to myself. So I wrote a letter to Nancy. The real thing. Sent it to her real address. I told her about the sequence of events involving Scott. Her initial response to that letter was 'Wow!' I thought that 'Wow!' would put the thing to rest. That Scott need never know.

"But there was something else, something deeper. And when I

decided I had an obligation to tell Scott, I wanted to protect him in any way I could from the discomfort he might feel. A straight guy's homophobia is just that—a mix of fear and ignorance. But a gay man's? Who knows homophobia more intimately?"

"A gay man's homophobia?" Betsy wrinkled her nose. "I'm not sure what you mean."

I repeated the face. "Talk about a catch-22. When I was growing up, it was like gay men weren't real men. They were—I don't know. Misshapen women. So if you were a man who liked men, who did you like? Not other gay men. They didn't count. And not straight men. That was a waste of time. So you start hating yourself. That low self-esteem, it can kill. I thought it would ruin my friendship with Scott. So I wrote my letters to him as though to Nancy, as if I'd absent-mindedly mixed up my correspondence, and with the title of the series on the outside of each envelope. It was all intended as a cushion. And that's why I wrote I was like that guy Yossarian in *Catch-22*. Even if Scott hadn't read the book, didn't get the reference, I could come back and explain it to him later."

"And have you?"

"No." I shook my head. "Not yet. Being with Scott, it's confusing, a unique experience for us both. He's always rushing off to work. The phone interrupts. There's never enough time."

"Never," Betsy agreed.

"More often than not, I end by making a joke."

"Relieves tension," Betsy said.

"Does," I nodded. "But that tension, it just shouldn't be. The friendship is all that matters—and you don't think about having sex with friends."

"You understand," Betsy said, "some people have trouble believing you can turn that sexual switch on and off like that."

"Jerry."

"So who is Jerry?"

"He's a friend. A gay man I know who works as an editor. He's read the letters and not only does he think that I'm lying about not wanting to have sex with Scott, he's convinced that Scott is gay."

"I see. And you're afraid that kind of reaction will make Scott feel all the more uncomfortable and further endanger your friendship."

"Exactly. I wish I could explain it to Scott so that he would understand that it shouldn't matter what anybody thinks. If I were uncomfortable any time somebody mistook me for a heterosexual, I'd be a nervous wreck."

Betsy smiled and said, "But you are a nervous wreck, Ed."

"And I had almost forgotten. Do people actually pay for this kind of treatment? But I'm serious, Betsy. Not only does it not make me feel uncomfortable to be mistaken for a straight man—it's fun in a perverse kind of way. Why doesn't it work the other way round?"

"I think you know why, Ed. Heterosexuality is still regarded by many people as the norm, with homosexuality abnormal, even subnormal. And, of course, immoral. A straight person may feel he's very cool about gay people, but not so cool about it that he can tolerate being mistaken for one. And this is probably more acutely the case with straight men than women."

"Jerry suggested he and I might get together for some weekend fun," I said. "Maybe I should send you in my place. Am I the only person who thinks my friendship with Scott can work?"

"I believe it can work," Betsy said. "I think it is working, and you should be proud of that. But consider Jerry's thoughts. I think you need to admit not having sex with Scott, that's part of your turmoil. Those sobbing fits. They're coming from somewhere."

"*Somewhere?*" I questioned. "It's not like I've never had a relationship that's soured before. But when I broke up with Jeff twenty-five years ago, even then I didn't wake up sobbing. And we lived together, shared the same bed every night. No piece of paper said it was so, but we went through the same ups and downs as any married couple. And what does the marriage vow say? Not forever. It says, 'till death us do part.'"

"What's your point?" Betsy looked confused. "The marriage vow doesn't come into it."

"Right," I said. "And given the divorce rate, I can't see that it carries much weight with opposite-sex couples either. But that *somewhere*, you think it's about time spent with Scott."

"No," Betsy insisted. "My point is that it's about intimate time you can't spend with Scott."

"But it's not," I said. "I know it's not. Falling for a straight man, trying to push it aside, that put me back in time, to a place before I met Jeff. That somewhere is still there, and however you cut it, it's 'don't ask, don't tell.' Not just the absence of a marriage vow, but all the trimmings. So much leftover crap, stuff Scott could never understand without my help."

"But Ed," Betsy's expression soured. "It's not your place. Scott came into the shop a browser in search of a book, not a crusader for civil rights. You can't force change. You can't impose friendship. And men have trouble asking for help. You know that from your experience with Patrick—and his problems became overwhelming. But more to the point, why would Scott *want* help from you on these issues? It's not like he'd run an ad in *The City Paper*: SWM seeking GWM."

"Of course not. And I didn't run an ad for GWM seeking SWM. But even if either of us had, neither would have paid attention to the other. It couldn't have been solicited or planned. It could only happen, and once it had, Scott and I both wanted to do the right thing. After all, if the suicide rate is still as high as it's ever been for gay men, then there are reasons for it. So you're either on the side that builds those reasons up, or you're on the side that breaks them down. I can't see why I should have been so afraid of letting Scott know how I feel—but I was terrified. It was as though, by simply trying to tell him, I'd committed a crime. I had to confront that terror, figure out where it was coming from, and bully it down once and for all—or my life is over, too. I owe it to Patrick. And I couldn't tell Scott, it seems, without his thinking I thought he was gay. Even if I did think that for a moment, why should it cause him so much discomfort? Unless he really is homophobic, afraid of even the slightest trace element of homosexuality in himself, as if it really *were* that loathsome a thing. And I can't be Scott's friend if he's homophobic. So I had to prove it to myself that he isn't."

Betsy stared through me, glassy-eyed, uneasy as that child confronted with a surprise exam, and she asked, "Have you proved it?"

"Proved it? How can you know? There's my sobbing fits. I still sense discomfort in Scott. But isn't that only natural, given what we need to overcome to remain friends? Romeo and Juliet had it easy; they only had to deal with Montagues and Capulets. And it's all happened so quickly. I met Scott in August, began writing those letters in mid-September. It's now the end of October."

"A whirlwind courtship," Betsy said.

"Yes," I smiled, recalling the warmth of Scott's hug. "And I haven't told you. I even got a hug out of Scott."

"Well," Betsy smiled, her brow rising like Jerry's. "What next? And how did you manage that?"

"Easy as buying a handgun. It was after Scott delivered the reprinted letters. We had a long talk, our longest yet. And I felt so right with life—I don't know that any heterosexual could understand. It was as though I'd gone back thirty years and made a correction. Scott could be who he is; I could be who I am. And we could remain close. I guess I needed a little more than a handshake to polish off our visit. And I did ask Scott's permission. And he gave it without hesitation."

"You know," Betsy said, "I'm looking forward to meeting this Scott. He must be one exceptional human being."

"He didn't mean to be quite so exceptional, but he's adjusted. And do you think if I was going to go to the trouble of falling in love I'd settle for less?"

"You might. I fell in love with a real loser once," Betsy confided. "And I knew he was a loser, but I was still in love. I think I would have stayed in love even though he might have brought my whole life down. But it didn't work out that way."

Betsy's tone and countenance shifted into a lower gear as the grandfather clock began its solemn chime. "He brought down his own life. Committed suicide very much like your friend, Patrick. He also jumped—cheap and sure. But from an overpass onto a highway during rush hour. If the fall didn't kill him, he rightly supposed, then one of twenty-six cars running over him would."

Betsy's head pivoted like an owl's. Noting the hour on the grandfather clock, she said, "Your time is up, Ed."

I looked at the face of the same clock, saw the hour was six, and said, "Were this a conventional fifty-minute session, my time would have been up ten minutes ago. But it's not, and the deal was that we would talk as friends. So, Kemosabe," the odd couple of Indian and masked man coming to mind. "What are friends for? Go on."

Betsy shifted uncomfortably in her chair, cleared her throat, and continued. "This was more than twenty-five years ago. I was nineteen. He was twenty-two, and so very beautiful. I looked plain as a pumpkin standing next to him. But it wasn't his eyes or anything about his appearance that first transfixed me. I was nearing the end of my freshman year in college, sophomore bound. And the first mild spring day, I took my lunch and a book outside. I hadn't known it before, but there was a grotto hidden away in back of the church on campus. I chanced on it that day—a kind of prefabricated niche with a statue of Mary inside looking out with her hands up in that way." Betsy put up her hands, palms outward, fingers extended. "Perfect kitsch. Benches, trees, a little stream ran quietly through the setting, the gentle hump of a bridge crossing it. I sat on one of the benches, eating my lunch, book open beside me. Halfway through my sandwich, I heard a man's voice coming from some place among the trees. He was reading Rilke. The ninth *Duino Elegy*, I later learned. Like you, I'd already been smitten by literature, but poetry did nothing for me. Until that moment. But he could have been reading *The Summit Sun*—anything—the way his voice held each word in place.

"I put down my sandwich, got up, and walked toward the sound like a sailor under a Siren's spell. I peeked through some bushes, trying not to be heard. When I caught my first glimpse of him sitting at his bench, hair lit from behind with sunlight, I was completely undone. He looked like he was wearing a halo. A male friend sat on the ground before him, his back to me, listening as intently as I was. The two of them together looked like a Pre-Raphaelite painting with a voiceover added for effect. And when the elegy ended, I walked around the bushes and introduced myself.

"The three of us became immediate good friends—the way it happens when you're young. And, of course, I was immediately smitten with Geoff—yes, that was his name. Geoff, though spelled the English way with a G. But Geoff had serious problems, and these were as apparent as was his beauty. I would only know him for twelve weeks. He was swiftly sliding into an alcoholic's routine. He may have had a mood disorder, but I wouldn't have known what that was then.

"We made love exactly one time. In that same grotto, at night. It was a good thing it was dark, or Mary would have blushed. Perhaps she did. I made most of the moves—something I ordinarily would never do. But that was the effect Geoff had on me. And I have always suspected that his real problem was that he was homosexual and wasn't able to deal with it. More than twenty-five years ago. You remember it well. After the suicide, his friend, the one who was there at the grotto the day we met—he dropped out of college and I never heard from him again. Twenty-five, thirty years ago. When you find the words, a plain yellow sheet can become a time machine.

"I don't talk about it. I've never told my children, keep waiting until they're a little older. My eldest graduated from high school this year, is only one year younger than I was that night Geoff and I made love. How old does a child have to be before he discovers his parents are human beings, too?" Betsy's eyes had slowly filled with tears, and they began to spill soundlessly down her cheeks.

"I'm sorry," I said. "I'm sorry if I provoked—"

"No. Nothing to be sorry about. I'm happy to remember. My love for Geoff is one of those things that belong to being nineteen. I'm glad I didn't miss it. I would give the experience to everyone if I could. I'm only sorry that Geoff couldn't find some way to deal with his problems. For him, Rilke wasn't enough.

"It was two years, six months, and twenty-one days after Geoff took his own life that I met my husband-to-be. I kept a journal then, so I could count the days. He was the first man to break the ice with me after Geoff's death, and even he had to chip away at it for a while. But he managed to do it, and came away with a good deal more than a hug. And we are very happily married.

"You know, a lot can be said for literature, for fiction, but you can always tell the difference between a true story and one that's been made up. Reading the letters you sent to Scott, understanding the strange way they came about, hearing of Scott and Amy, you and Jeff—Patrick's suicide. I kept thinking as I was reading, I've known all these people, every one of them. They just go by different names. And even the names aren't so different.

"When you called me at home this morning, I was sitting there thinking about calling you. I jumped in my chair when I heard the phone ring, thought I was in my office and answered in my business voice. Ever have that experience? Like waking from a dream, not remembering where you were."

"Sure," I said. "Happens to me all the time."

"Yeah?" Betsy questioned, then put aside any doubt. "I'll bet it does."

She opened a drawer in the mahogany desk, pulled out the bound copy of my letters, and laid it on the wooden surface between us. "You know, Ed," the ringed edge of the black and white binder seemed to stare and blink at me. "We all engage in camouflage, put on one face for one place, then another for the next. But while I read your letters, it was as though the need for camouflage disappeared. Odd, the way they begin and end. Nearly a hundred pages sandwiched between two short letters written directly to Scott. Like bookends. Almost too perfect."

"A long-delayed response," I said.

"A catharsis," Betsy suggested.

"Maybe," I said, but thought better of it. "More like a misplaced poem."

Betsy smiled, the irony of a final tear falling to the mahogany desk. "Rereading that first letter to Scott this morning, I'd been reminded that there really are all kinds of families. Not just mom and pop and two point three—but all kinds. And that you're there at the shop each day at seven-thirty. I wanted to tell you that I hope you regard me as part of that family."

"I'm not sure," I said, taking the packet of letters into my hands, "if I can take credit or responsibility for all that went into these letters. I hardly feel I wrote them. And I've always thought it was the patient in this kind of situation who's supposed to break down in tears."

"You've read too many books, Ed. The older I get the less of a distinction I see between patient and doctor. One day I'm on this side of the couch, so to speak, the next day I'm laid out on it. You'd be surprised what can happen in an office such as this one."

"And you'd be surprised," I said, "what can happen in a bookshop."

"Once upon a time, perhaps," Betsy said. "Nevermore."

I don't know how much it had to do with my single impromptu meeting with Betsy, but I slept well that night and Halloween arrived cool and clear and without a sobbing session. I could only hope I was done with them.

It is often dark in the early morning when I walk from my Philadelphia apartment through Schuylkill Park on my way to the train and the bookshop it is to take me to. The few dogs I encounter then are shadowy figures chasing stick, or ball, or each other, their masters cast in shadow, too, with only the occasional dot flare of orange as a cigarette is pumped upon. A dog will stop to concentrate on his morning's business, then trot along while his human companion is left behind to clean up the mess, causing me to wonder who the genuine master is in this hierarchy. Sometimes I am greeted warmly by the auburn shape of Little Bit, named so because of her stubby legs. Or I am nearly run over by an enthusiastic Labrador who has gotten the hang of the gas pedal but not the brake. Daisy, a white and wiry terrier set low to the ground and ripe for picking, behaves like a high school tease. She never allows me to pet her but runs very nearly up to me, then veers abruptly, circling wider and wider, as if I were pole to her tether ball. Her master suggests she is intimidated by the book bag I carry, best known as a receptacle for pens and yellow pads, lesser for its crumb deposits, the remnants of a thousand lunches. But the same bag that appears to intimidate Daisy is eagerly poked into by a beagle whose affection shows no bias—unless you happen to be a squirrel.

On this particular morning I crossed paths with a golden retriever who ignored me in his dizzying pursuit of falling autumn leaves. Their abundance was so great, the hue of dog and leaf interchangeable, so that I pictured the retriever collapsing pounds lighter late that same day—the inexhaustible game of tag still incomplete.

But the greatest canine concentration of any part of my given days comes nearer its conclusion when I am making the reverse trek through Schuylkill Park on my evening return from the shop. The timing of this walk is in perfect sync with the airing of my neighbors' dogs, en masse, and none greets me with more effusive style than does Eli.

Eli is a rare breed, some sort of middle European mountain dog whose look is a cross between St. Bernard and rottweiler. For size, coat, and face picture St. Bernard; for coloring think rottweiler. His master is the sculptor Eric Berg, whose bronze *Grizzly* graces Fitler Square only a block away from the park. This smaller-than-life bear, set down on all fours and mounted on marble, has darkened with time. All of him, that is, except for the tufts of his ears, rubbed sunny with affection by the children who routinely ride him, hoisted by their obliging elders. We adults could do no better than to observe the simpler diversions of dogs and children.

Early on in our liaisons, when Eric would spot me and my book bag coming up the walk, he got in the habit of instructing Eli to sic what he'd mistaken for a lawyer's valise. Eli is the ever-dutiful son, cocking his head to the heavens and letting out a slow, curdling Baskerville howl. He then proceeds to gallop toward me with a lopsided gait that gets low grades for form but is rich in cuteness. Eric says it's an attack that sends any undesirable from the door of his household, but it is entirely bluff. When Eli reaches me, the gruff demeanor dissolves, and I am drenched in his wet kisses and he in my adoring strokes. Though I am tempted to return the licks, I have yet to master the furball process.

The routine of this evening spate of canines is a great mix of human and dog kind, a brief orgy of neighborliness giving weight to the city's name: Brotherly Love. Here in the park set between river and residences, I have observed few serious skirmishes. I once saw a dog take off angrily after a jogger, who quickly complained, "That animal *ought* to be on a leash." To which I thought, "Why not leash the jogger?" I've been snapped at myself, have regularly seen one dog snap at another because of an unwanted sexual advance, and am routinely barked at. This barking, however, is usually of the mixed-metaphor variety, with the dog's tail wagging at the behind. But one day not long ago I was witness to something of a genuinely warlike nature.

Of all the dogs who frequent the park, Eli has the greatest bulk. There is one Great Dane who stands an inch or two higher, but for sheer mass Eli has him easily whipped. His bark, too, is a commanding bulk, calling each lesser dog to attention. But while the advance gives Eli the apparent manner of a beast, there is something in his breeding that knows only how to give way to beauty.

All the more startling when one calm, weather-delicious evening in the park, another dog half his stature began to attack Eli with repeated blows. Eli didn't know what to make of it, any more than did I in my approach looking on. Whatever had provoked the smaller dog was invisible to me, but it was clear this was no bit of play-acting: the dog meant business. He made sharp, elliptical lunges, growled, and struck at Eli with the viciousness of a shark in bloodied waters. At the third or fourth orbit, Eli turned on the other dog, lifted his lips to show the gum line and the full fury of his canine's canines, and made a quick chomp into the air. Though I stood twenty feet from the scene, I instinctively backed away, my image of him changing abruptly in that snapshot moment. It was as if the sweet "Jesus loves you this I know" of childhood had come upon the busy Temple where His temper flared, tipping tables in His wake. The episode then broke into a real battle, tight as two boxers confined to a ring with neither dog bending to the will of the other. Eli had the obvious advantage, but the smaller dog was more supple and at ease in his role. With the escalation, everyone else in the park froze in place, *La Grande Jatte* minus monkey and parasols. A genuine serpent, foul-mouthed and venomous, had entered this Eden, and any bite finding its mark would draw more than apple juice. The conflict lasted only seconds in real time, but unexpected violence can lift the moment from the present and extend it.

The shock then fell with the same speed it had arisen, and the sparring partners were separated, gradually calmed by their masters. Eden regained, the quieter dramas that had filled the park turned again, as if the nickel setting *La Grande Jatte* in motion had found its slot.

I cautiously approached Eric in the hope of not being mistaken for Eli's adversary. Eli looked up at me, still panting out the rage the other dog had provoked. Bewildered and sad-eyed, he now seemed to be asking of me in the voice of one of the Supremes, "Where did our love go?"

"What was that all about?" I asked in return, uncertain whether I was addressing Eli or Eric.

"We're not sure." It was Eric who answered. "But it's happened before. We think Eli brings out the herding instinct in the other dog. That because of Eli's size and shape he is being mistaken for a cow."

Having grown up on a dairy farm where the herding of cows had been a daily ritual in the warm-weather months, I recognized the probable correctness of the theory at once. We'd had a series of collies over the years, and I'd occasionally witnessed in horror the over-zealousness of an otherwise gentle breed in herding. The decapitation of a cow's udder was not unheard of, a kind of mutilation that makes the skin crawl even in these nipple-piercing times. But never before had I heard of one dog mistaking another for its cattle. Yet here was the evidence set down directly before my eyes, whether I believed in it or not.

OTHER HOLIDAYS MAY have remained the same, but if you want to look at the changing character of America, look to Halloween. Christmas, it is true, has been criticized for having become over-commercialized. But that analysis was already a popular one, likely an old one, when I was growing up in the wilds of Wisconsin forty years ago. I recall an aunt in Milwaukee complaining that before she set out her jack-o-lantern, the local department store with the Jewish name had put up their Santa Claus. But I am more likely to fault those who don't recognize that there is a profit motive in all things than I am those who see the advantage at Christmas of taking a little from the rich to make the poor a little richer. That, I have always been under the impression, is part of the message. And nowhere have I heard it told what the baby Jesus did with all that gold, frankincense, and myrrh. Particularly the gold, since I wouldn't know what to do with either frankincense or myrrh. And people still drink champagne on New Year's and green beer on St. Patty's, go in for pastels come Easter, and for red, white, and blue on the Fourth of July.

But Halloween. Even before I leave the bookshop in the late afternoon, early trick-or-treaters—children no more than five or six years of age and tottering in costumes too bulky for their tiny frames—are already infiltrating the maze of Summitt's streets. In the old days we waited till dark before sauntering forth in something simple as a discarded bed sheet, holes cut at the appropriate places. But now the night is an unsafe place, and spooks are not the danger. More likely the danger comes from those in sheets with holes cut at inappropriate places. And way back then it seems to have occurred to no one to tamper with the goods often handed out by perfect strangers.

Though then it also seemed that every adult I knew instinctively knew every other adult, as though a web were already in place, and that a stranger could be found only at the end of a long journey. It was a world not linked by three major networks, but by what at least passed for genuine concern. Bread and canned goods put up at home, hand-rolled cigarettes, and milk served still warm from the cow's breast. Small-time commerce all belonging to the fixed income of family, friends, and routine. I don't believe it was a better world, but a child's clock ticks at a different pace, so that a summer's vacation fell just short of eternity, while the character of its inhabitants rose to the angelic. The sun shone brighter, thunderstorms were fiercer, and holiday decorations were carefully put away each year to be hauled out the next and the next. Somehow this successive handling of sentimental objects purchased at five-and-dime stores when things there could be had for fives and dimes made those objects finer, even if they'd been made of the cheapest materials. The investment principle was simple. Each asked no more than the slightest touch at the proper moment in the year, their luster increased by the residue of hands that held them. In keeping this custom, a twofold return was promised per annum (its dividend more assured than any stock market). The sense of antiquity was private, inestimable, and could not be translated to the auction block. But like all things sent out in time, they were part passing illusion. One day an ornament would slip from its hold, fall to the floor, and crack. Were a replacement found, this Johnny-come-lately was viewed with suspicion, his sheen too proud to sit among heirlooms.

We have, of course, long since overshot the world of three major networks and have come to the age of designer television where you can spend half your evening trying to figure out what to watch, then end by watching nothing better. Progress, it would seem, is a place never gotten to, the surface sheer. Not white-shirt white, but transparent, the invisible past haunting each of us, no matter how far into the future we stray.

Now with Halloween the costumes are largely media-inspired mermaids and beasts, their routes so carefully planned no one will chance on a stranger's door, though even this is no guarantee contraband won't turn up in the candy corn. And since Summitt's last outdoor toilet was moved indoors several decades previous, what's left for the innocents to topple? Ghosts in broad daylight, treats in need of x-raying before consumption, the gurgle of flush toilets. Might as well skip Halloween and go directly to Thanksgiving.

But on the sunny side of All Hallow's Eve 1998, something very much like a pair of unsheeted though fully clothed ghosts would appear at the door of Bound Matters.

I was born of Finnish descent, both sides, so along with some of the more distinguished breeds populating Schuylkill Park, you could say I am a purebred. In the case of Finland, I don't know where this puts me on anything like a nobility scale. About the country's only world-famous personages are probably the composer Jean Sibelius and that architect whose name I can never recall. And perhaps the language itself, bearing little relation to any other, sprung from the cold and isolation of the region. Judging from the deeds done by which people get their names into newsprint, obscurity may be the better choice. But like most Americans, I am of a wayward ancestry. My kinfolk having drifted, I grew up many hundreds of miles south of the Arctic Circle, a quarter way round the globe. It was there by the shores of Gitchee Gumee that we used to tell a joke upon ourselves:

> Q: Did you hear about Russia's new zoo?
> A: They put a fence around Finland.

Ethnic jokes are now forbidden in public, as though what defines the individual can only be met with a stony face, even confined to the closet the way a malformed child was in less enlightened times. Like Eliza Doolittle at her de-cockneyed debut, best we limit public discourse to the weather—though weather, too, has proven a sensitive issue in recent years, adding to the collective gloom. We require privacy, yes. The nest for familial intimacy. The preferred house of worship or none at all. The book of our own choosing. But what of the separateness a good joke can help dissolve? Our privacy has resonance largely because we carry the thought of one another there. Were this not so, Dear Reader, you would likely have given up on me many pages before. We are a single people, sprung from a very large bang, but having scattered in so many directions, we often don't recognize the friend we pass each day in the street. Our potential better half might be found anywhere.

So it happened that on this Halloween morning there arrived at the bookshop an older couple who appeared out of touch with the demands of both political correctness and the simplest courtesy. I greeted them at the door in my usual manner, but my greeting was instantly mistaken for a sales pitch.

The feminine half of the team rebuffed me, saying, "We know what we want, so don't try and sell us something."

I took my place at the counter.

The lady—cheerless, squat, lumbering—took up the lead. Were she one of the cows from my Wisconsin childhood, she would be the one called Bossy. Accompanying her was a taller man who nevertheless seemed to hunch at her request so as to appear smaller. Visibly older, he trailed as though leashed, the two heading up the center aisle of the shop. They settled finally at the rack of paperback mysteries toward the back. There they would fumble among the stacks for a good twenty minutes. I should say the lady fumbled, occasionally sputtering: "I've already read this one. Why do they keep changing the covers?" Or, "What's the matter with her? Why hasn't she written anything new?" Or, "This'll never do—what I want is a polite murder in the library." All the while, the man quietly oversaw the selection proceedings, not only leashed but apparently muzzled as well.

Having made her choices, the lady headed toward the register, in her arms a load of paperbacks, the old man toddling empty-handed in tow. Turning to him, she asked as an afterthought, "Don't you want anything, dear?" No response came, so the lady answered her own question. "I thought not."

Each wore a hat. The lady's hat, a millinery equivalent of its owner, was an ambiguous gray felt job covered in pins that bore place names, the probable souvenirs of a lifetime of journeying. A single pheasant's feather struck a proud salute among the pins.

"Now don't show me any of your expensive hardbacks," the lady fired me a warning as she plopped her books on the counter. "I like a good paperback mystery before bed. None of those bloody thrillers, mind you, but a straightforward murder. Puts me to sleep."

Loosening the muzzle of my imagining, the old man grumbled, "Keeps me awake."

I stared at the dark green hat the man wore. Rigid and vaguely military, it made a single statement, a caption I heard myself read aloud: "United States Forest Service." Then, trying to remain pleasant among the unpleasantness, I chirped, "I grew up in the North Woods."

"Where?" the lady asked.

"Northern Wisconsin. On a small farm near a river called the Brule."

The couple looked at one another, visibly astonished, the first meaningful exchange between them since they'd entered the shop. Another ancient veil had been lifted, and it was finally my turn to announce, "You may now kiss the bride."

"We lived just outside of Cornucopia for many years," the lady said, her voice warming like sunshine. "My husband here took a job with the Forest Department there. In summer we went to the Brule often. To fish. To swim. To picnic."

Then it must have been I who looked astonished as the couple happily replayed memories of idyllic Wisconsin summers. Before my eyes they'd been transformed into two excited children telling bits of the same story in leapfrog fashion.

"And the skies," the lady said, waving an arm above her head like a fairy godmother dousing the room in stardust.

"And the skies..." the gentleman concurred. "There is nothing like a Wisconsin sky."

As they went on rhapsodically, I revisited for the first time in years that little town with the inappropriate name of Cornucopia. Brideshead it wasn't, notable—as it was—for a muddle of leaky shacks, an Indian Reservation that somehow managed to sprout TV antennae in the late 1950s. Each autumn we would pass through it in the family Chevrolet on our way to Bayfield in search of apples. My elders would shake their heads at the Indian shacks and wonder aloud how anyone could live "like that."

"Look," someone would inevitably say, "they got television but not an indoor toilet!" It seems my elders had already forgotten that the house I was born into originally had no television and that the pot-to-piss-in was out back in a separate, unheated building, given the climate about as great an architectural folly as can be imagined. But upward mobility, I have found, can be forgetful. Like that.

Many years later, in Paul Fussell's book entitled *Class*, I read the theory posed that the wealthier the American household, the more difficult it is to find the television within. In such a class structure, it makes perfect sense for the Indians of the 1950s to have brought their televisions indoors before they thought of doing the same with the toilet, and to put it front and center as it was likely their greatest expenditure.

But in the 1950s I'd no knowledge that a class structure lingered in America. I'd been taught something closer to the opposite, that it was the guts and bold intelligence of free enterprise, the sweat of labor, not the birth luck of privilege, that had brought about the American Dream. I trusted history texts in that same way some patrons of bookshops trust dust-jacket blurbs. Nor did I know anything about the ever-lengthening trail of lies and broken promises that had put the Indians aside on increasingly smaller parcels of land, little more than concentration camps without ovens. I was ignorant in the way a child is, and wise in the ways that children are before the simplicity of their games is transformed by the duplicity of adult schemes. I did sense there was something wrong in Cornucopia, but at my elders' suggestion I probably put the blame on the Indians themselves. It was their choice to sell out the whole of Manhattan for Cracker Jack trinkets and blankets—or was it twenty-four bucks? For such weak-minded dealings alone, they deserved their fate. How could I have guessed that the stories had been whitewashed to fit the moral sense of the audience who would hear them, and that I was the next duped spectator in line for the show?

As if she'd heard this aside, the lady in the bookshop complied: "That's Injun country," sending my uncertain glance from sci-fi, to romance, to historical fiction, where I half expected the last of the Mohicans to launch an attack. When no retribution came, I nodded in quiet agreement. Still, I imagined, most of the Europeans settling there thought of the land as free for the taking, even that its former tenant, the Injun, was out of step and rightly ghetto-bound. In Cornucopia he no longer slept in his native tepee or hogan, but in a shack that suggested neither ethnicity nor lifestyle, but read only *poor*. If this were an example of Darwinian fitness, there was something sinister in its twist, a story where the strong had prevailed and so weakened the host that he, too, had been seduced by the easy company of Lucy and Ethel, Ricky and Fred.

But there was a once-upon-a-time when this entire nation had been Injun country. And before that saber-toothed tiger and mammoth country. And before that...and before that. We might all be called transients, renters mistaken for owners. But that is not the mystery which needs solving for me. Rather, it is the impolite manner of the evictions and the subsequent cover-ups. No politician, writer of textbooks, or Bible-thumper, however clever, can wipe the fossil record clean. No paper-shredder built by fallible man is so thorough. Something remembers. A crow overhead, unnoticed, is witness. And how I can hear him laugh each morning on my way to the shop:

"Haaaa..."

"Haaaa..."

"Haaaa...."

He knows my pride and my vanity inside out. And he knows the love I feel that would have me transcend all that pride and vanity so as to rise in the morning like a golden sun. But in a crow's laughter I sense there is the knowledge that this, too, can only hold in place for the moment, teeter there, then fall with a thud and a crack.

Hearing neither thud nor crack, the gentleman's wife went on. "We loved it dearly, but did not think of retiring there. It's a cruel country, too, the winters brutal. A major event in that season was a trip to the grocery."

I remembered well the paralysis of a Wisconsin winter and smiled within, happy to be in the presence of someone who might understand why I had not chosen to remain in such a beautiful place. The wealthy there, whose large summer homes dotted the banks of the Brule, were fair-weather friends who never came before fishing season began or stayed beyond the early snows of late autumn.

But my roots went deep enough so that I remained for twenty years through all the four seasons, finally too poor to stay, yet not rich enough to return only in the warmer months. It was then I attained a kinship to the Wandering Jew with an only apparently shallow root that repeats of a less-spoken holocaust and the label of a pink triangle:

"We can forgive, but we must never forget."

And the crack that first let that Injun light into my particular forest came to me in the voice of Buffy Sainte-Marie. That distinctive tremor—the mix of passion, humor, and anger—pierced my adolescent consciousness as unswervingly as would Proust a decade later.

It is the shamans who say that all that is truly alive is contained in a circle that never dies. And though death, I believe, is as much part of that circumference as birth, he nourishes the living along with the yet-to-come. *How could it be that the one should exist, but not the other?* So it would seem that Buffy, too, had helped prepare me for the shock of a fall from a high place and the white-sleeved arm put out to help me up.

In the bookshop, closing out the sale of paperback mysteries the lady had brought to the counter, I watched the gentleman put his arm through the circle of her own, the two linked again as they had been all those summers before. And the lady asked me, "Do you have the latest Dick Francis?"

"Yes," I answered, "but the latest is only available in hardcover."

"That's all right," she said. "Throw it on the pile. There's always room for a Dick Francis. And you're such a nice young man."

MUCH LIKE THE city kid who grows up in a world of asphalt, high-rise, and heavy traffic and dreams of escaping to an ever-greener suburb, I, a country boy, set his grass-is-always-greener sights on a city. And like the city kid who learns that with greener environs comes the downside of mosquitoes, allergic reaction, a landscape riddled with Lyme-disease-bearing ticks, and a lawn in perpetual need of mowing, this country boy never discovered an urban setting that matched the gleaming El Dorado of his imagination. But the apparently opposing journeys of country mouse and city mouse are no longer at odds, having been reconciled in the slow realization that the complacency of a gilded destination is not half so rich as the adventure taking us there.

So in accord with a dream, its liberty, and the pursuit of some happiness, I now live near the heart of a city set between two rivers, the Delaware and the Schuylkill. City of neighborhoods, of white-steepled Christ Church, Betsy Ross, Ben Franklin, and fourteen other signers of the Declaration of Independence. Not those Founding Fathers I'd conjured up on an overheated day, but the genuine articles.

It had been a long-standing tradition of this historic place that no building should rise higher than the statue of William Penn atop City Hall. But when in the 1980s that tradition was broken, it was as though an aggressive bull had found a single hole in the fence, and the entire herd had followed.

Overnight the skyline grew, swift as bamboo, and now you need to hunt for Billy Penn among the fresh crop of steely shoots. It could be he prefers his newly won privacy, even the pipsqueak status, for I have heard few complaints.

It happens I am a lover of traditions. Like signposts in the circle of a year, they tie us to the past and keep the present from leaking messily into the future. But when a tradition is made unalterable, it can become lifeless as words of a dead language. In pursuit of an idiom that swells with life's joys, buckles under its burdens, then rises again, I would add that any declaration of independence worth its salt inevitably contains seeds of revolutions to come.

It was the architecture that first drew me to the part of the city I now call home. The brownstones, the heavy facades of Frank Furness, all the grand townhouses set discretely back from the street and gated in wrought iron. They seemed like urban Manderleys to me, each with the hope of an accompanying Max de Winter, library, and warming fire within. On less-hopeful days I see my neighborhood for the has-been it has become. Its brownstones, after all, were intended as single-family dwellings replete with servants' quarters. Now they are haphazardly broken into apartments, often with little regard for the integrity of the original structure. Democracy, in effect, reducing one man's castle to another's condo.

But on yet another day I have seen the city shine. Crossing the bridged Schuylkill on my morning walk to the train, the river's water swollen with rain, I have stopped to watch the yellow sun climb those recently man-made peaks to the east. All appears new, as if the previous night's rain had put down a fresh coat of paint on the planet whole. The sky is awash with remnants of storm, and I pivot to take in the entire picture. As the sun caps the steely horizon, I've witnessed the air shot golden in every direction, as though Midas had tapped the very atmosphere.

ON A COLD NOVEMBER MORNING, even before I had a chance to snap on the radio, Scott arrived at the shop, a brown paper-cupped coffee in a white plastic sleeve steaming in each of his hands. He awkwardly pulled open the glass door as I walked up the center aisle to meet him there. Once inside he put forth both question and cup, the latter a redundant extension of his own white-sleeved arm.

"Black?"

I nodded *yes*, taking the warm cup into my hands as the door slid quietly shut behind him.

"Sorry I've not been in," Scott said. "Things have been hectic at the printshop, but they're easing up now." With his left hand he lifted the sleeve on his right arm and gave the wristwatch beneath a glance. "I have some extra time this morning."

"Gotta make hay when the sun shines," I said. "It's what we used to say on the farm."

"You lived on a farm?"

"Grew up on a farm—could've sworn I told you."

Scott shook his head.

I looked into his eyes as if to hold them there with care, the way you would the tenderest part of a man's anatomy. "That's the way it is," I said. "Each of us thinking the other's been told, when half the time we're talking to ourselves." Putting my coffee cup into my left hand, I closed the fingers on my right and waved it palm to face so as to break the spell of my gaze. "There. You look ordinary now. Just another five-and-dime-a-dozen, nice-looking guy who knows how to press a white shirt."

"I confess." Scott cast me a puckish grin. "I have it done out." He lifted the plastic lid of his coffee cup and took a sip.

Returning my cup to the right hand, I took a reciprocal sip and toasted, "To a friendship made in Heaven."

"You know," Scott said, "when I consented to being your friend I didn't think—how could I have guessed? I'm still not entirely comfortable with it."

"*Quid pro*—" I began. "That proverb, what is it?"

"*Quid pro quo*," Scott answered. "I had three years of Latin."

"Right. And I'm not really comfortable with it either. But while you've been pursuing Mrs. Matthews these months, I've been time-traveling."

"Don't know what you mean." Scott tipped his head to one side.

"Why should you?" I asked, tipping my head to the other. "When you picked up the last two sets of Proust, it was like you pushed me through a door. It must have opened onto a bottomless shaft. I've been in freefall ever since.

"So bring me back, Scott. Give us an update. Any sign of Mrs. Matthews?"

Again Scott shook his head.

"Then how goes the reading group?"

"Okay, I guess," Scott shrugged. "I'm about two hundred pages into *Swann's Way*. My friend Beth, she's furthest along. And she really likes it. But the rest. They're still having trouble."

"As I thought," I said. "Though I'm glad to hear you're sticking with it. You take commitment seriously." I smiled, a glint of pride in my voice. "I saw a bumper sticker in my neighborhood the other day. It read: 'Thelma and Louise—Live!' That's my neighborhood."

Scott grinned all the more, then removed the plastic lid from his coffee cup and took a larger swallow. As if bolstered by the brew, he replaced the lid and said, "There is something I need today. A dictionary."

"Dictionary?" I questioned, the familiar word sounding foreign.

"Yeah. The one I have at the printshop is ancient, falling apart." Scott looked up from his coffee cup. "You do sell dictionaries?"

"Yes, of course."

"Any recommendations?"

"*The American Heritage.*" I didn't hesitate. "Good type. Well-illustrated. Current. Even a little funky. Let me show you." I walked to the counter and put my coffee cup down behind it, then went over to the reference shelf on the opposite side of the shop. I pulled out a large volume and hauled it to a table near the center of the room. Resting the heavy tome among the lifestyle books, I let it fall open randomly.

"See?" I said, my hand pointing to the two-page spread.

Scott had followed me and peered at the open book, each page a double column of words and definitions flanked by a wide margin of illustrations. "Nice," he said. "But way too much book. I need something portable."

"Comes in paperback," I said, "though that's not so complete." To further my point, I suggested we look up *friendlily*, and flipping to the page, pressed my finger to the entry. "It's all there," I announced: "Friend. Friendly. Friendlier. Friendlily." Stammering on the last word, I scolded myself, "Should've had one of these in my apartment when I was writing those letters. All the F words anyone could want."

My physician-heal-thyself speech suspended, I could hear Scott's laughter, as though cocooned, but I'd not gotten my own joke. I had been distracted by the tiny portrait that loomed suddenly large on the opposite page. There, in stern three-quarter profile, was Sigmund Freud, his eyes fired by a missionary zeal. Now I was the one seized by the tenderest part of a man's anatomy, and in knee-jerk response, a cartoon bubble rose atop Freud's steely cameo, the words within its circle forming:

There are no accidents.

I shuddered, then slammed the book shut, a great thud stinging the quiet.

"What's wrong?" Scott asked, alarmed, nothing false in his concern. "What happened?"

Without thinking, I flung myself at Scott, gave him an unexpected hug, then backed off, my action so swift he had no time to react.

"It's nothing," I said, my voice apologetic. "The coffee. I had two strong mugs before coming to work. Shouldn't begin a third. Makes me edgy."

But sensing a cover-up, I withdrew the claim, saying, "No. That's not it either." Uncertain, I cupped my right hand. "You know, Scott," I rested the same hand on the crotch of my pants. "It doesn't hurt here." I lifted the hand and let it graze my temple. "But here." The hand settled finally on my left breast. "And especially here."

Scott's gaze had followed this sign of the cross no farther than my crotch. It stuck there in shock, like the over-expressive face of a silent filmstar. And wanting to bring talk back to the pictures, I imagined myself saying, *Don't look at my crotch, you've no business looking at my crotch!* But the words didn't sound, only played out in my head. Twisting my body away, I looked dejectedly at the lavish design books crowding the table, my glance settling on the spot where Scott had put his coffee cup moments before. It had overturned, the warm contents dripping at the edges of a book about log home construction. In the same instant Scott and I reached out to right the wrong, our hands meeting, then joining, at the empty cup.

"Sorry," said Scott, clutching my hand. "Sorry I ruined the book. I'll pay."

"Forget it," I said. "Probably knocked over the cup when I hugged you."

"I shouldn't," Scott rebuked himself. "Should never put anything down on a book."

We seesawed like two gentlemen, each shaking the other's hand, until I said, "Maybe we should both lay off the caffeine."

Our hands parted.

"But I," my arm fell to my side, "I've been time-traveling. Going back to places I didn't even know were still there. Your being exactly who you are—that's helped me more than any therapist." I smiled. "Maybe I should be paying you."

"For what?" Scott refused to return the smile. "The guy I met last summer, he was cheerful. Now look at you." Scott put out his hand and righted the coffee cup at the same place it had spilled. "Damage done," he concluded. "Don't you think it would be better, so much easier, if I switch to being an evening customer?"

"But time-traveling," I said, "it's like going through the mourning process. Can't skip a thing. Cheat on any part of the deal and you'll only have to go back and start over." I looked into a far corner of the shop as though the walls meeting there had disappeared. Briefly joining the distance, I returned with a question and said, "So what if . . . ?"

"What if what?"

"What if, twenty-five years ago, Jeff and I had married—like you and Amy might have?"

"Ed. You're no special case. Death, taxes, and getting your heart busted. Amy and I didn't pull it off either."

"Might have," I held. "Could have. But twenty-five years ago same-sex unions read like science fiction."

"Change," Scott stumbled on the word. "That will change."

Oblivious to the claim, I charged, "The Church said we'd broken God's laws and the American Psychiatric Association—they went so far as to say we were ill. Fit for sex, perhaps, but never love."

"Why lecture me, Ed?"

"My own parent insisted I did not belong—"

"I'm on your side."

"That I would need to go elsewhere."

"They're all wrong," Scott said, arms meeting at his wrists like a cross. "As far as I'm concerned, you can marry who you please." The cross crumbling, he flung his hands in opposite directions. "But it won't be me."

"I never proposed marriage. Only friendship."

"It's crazy. Whoever needed to propose friendship?"

"I did, Scott. To weather change you put up a shelter. And you took to it. You said *yes*."

"What if I've changed my mind?"

"It's a man's prerogative," I said, "but if you're thinking about splitting, don't let me be the last to know. Been there. Done all that. A marriage without status. A divorce no more than a divide.

"And why—*how* could you know what it meant to come out twenty-five years ago? You were—what? Seven. I can tell you the passage was nothing like a debutante's. Social life played out under the fluorescent light of a public restroom. Maybe a street corner. Wherever the rumor told you men picked up men. Imagine hunting Mrs. Matthews there. The gay bar scene, that's as good as it got."

"I don't need to hear this," Scott put his hands to his ears.

"Those bars," I said, again oblivious to protests, "they were as exclusively homosexual as the world outside them was said to be exclusively heterosexual. And each of those two ways of looking at reality is a lie, every bit as ugly as separate drinking fountains for blacks and whites. And think of it, Scott. I could have spent my whole life frequenting gay bars and would never have met you."

"That's right," Scott said pointedly, "I've never been inside a gay bar."

"Really? Then you've missed one of life's most beautiful ironies: to hear a chorus of fired-up gay men gathered around a piano singing 'There is nothing like a dame.'"

"And come Sunday," Scott quashed a laugh, "you won't find me in a Protestant church either. But that's not because I have anything against Protestants. It's a bird-of-a-feather thing."

"Of course." My head began a slow nod as I intoned the French equivalent, "*La cage aux folles.*" To the tick of this metronome, I felt an aged ornament slip from my hand. "Damage done."

"Damage?" Scott quarreled. "Big deal. Some spilled coffee. Nothing my Am Ex can't handle."

"No?" The crease in my brow deepened. "The divide is wide," and hearing the rhyme, I said, "You know, I used to write a lot of poetry."

"Who cares about poetry? Not me."

"In adolescence," I pretended not to hear, "in my own—that same script of Amy's. The writing of a tender poem...." I hesitated. "It became an almost masturbatory device."

"That's enough," Scott cut into my words. "It's none of my business."

"Then whose—whose business is it?"

"Nobody's. That's private."

"And what if," my time machine whirled into the future, "what if little Scottie Junior turns out to be gay?"

"That won't—" Scott stopped, gave the shop door an anxious glare, then made a correction. "That's none of *your* business."

"Don't tell," I said, almost to myself, then dropped my words, one by one, like stones into a well. "Don't even ask."

Scott's eyes resting nowhere, he said, "You pressure me, Ed. Like a belligerent child you pressure me."

"Child?" I questioned. "I'm fifteen years your senior. I would like to think I've reached a certain maturity. That we might not be friends—okay. No promises, it happens. But if we cannot be, that's intolerable to me."

My eyes fell on the handprinted booklist on the counter. "Though you don't care for poetry, you should be curious about my next project."

"Why?" Scott made a face. "What's in it for me?"

"In it? Yes, you are. You're a character. Those letters I wrote, the copies you made. I intend to rework them, flesh out the story and set it in this bookshop where we met."

"Bookshop? You mean here? But I'm not comfortable—"

"Forget your discomfort," I interrupted. "This isn't about a bad back. Do you think it was discomfort Patrick felt? Imagine his despair."

"Why should I?" Scott fired back. "It'll only bring me down. And I never even met Patrick. How could I know what he felt? What I mean is that I'm not comfortable about your writing about us. What if someone thinks—?"

"Nobody's gonna think that. And I'll change things, turn the town of Summitt, PA, upside down." An image like a tattered engraving jutted into mind. "There's a cemetery in Old City. Down by the Delaware. I'm sure you know it. The headstones toppling, their names so weather-worn you can't read a word. That's how my book will be. A love story carved from the love of story. But smudged, deliberately smudged to make a point. And it's in part my love for you."

I stopped and looked directly at Scott, his head stricken with a tremor that seemed to say, *When you look at me, when our eyes meet, I don't know what you're thinking.*

As if I'd heard the thought spoken aloud, I answered, "I want you to know one thing, Scott, and to understand it clear to the bottom. I don't think about having sex with you. I can't. It would be like sex with a sibling, or fooling around with a friend of twenty years. No pleasure there. About the only fantasy I've had concerning you is that I might be best man at your wedding. Farfetched, sure. I'm an upstart, and you probably already have a long-standing friend in mind for the role. It's just a wish, one you make at the sight of a falling star. But what would be a bit part for someone else would be a leading role for me."

Scott was again looking me directly in the eye, and I asked, "Do you believe me?" He looked away, then back, and said,

"You're not making sense, Ed. If you never think about us having sex, why would you go to so much trouble to make me think you do?"

"Because you didn't understand my first letter," I answered. "I had thought that by merely writing in a tender voice, one you weren't used to hearing from another man, you'd realize my situation—but you didn't get it. What could I do? I felt I'd been dishonest. I couldn't sleep. I wanted our friendship to be genuine, open. So I hatched my plot. I would send a series of letters. From the beginning I planned to hint at sex, but I would only imply, and you would follow, as in a dance, by inferring. An odd approach to the oldest of rituals. Yet I never intended to so much as proposition you, much less to follow through. But in putting myself in that strange position—writing as if to Nancy even though I knew it was you who'd be doing the reading—

there was much I came to learn that I hadn't gotten either. It was as though I'd put on another personality, or acquired a third eye, and things far away came to meet me there. What I wanted you to understand is that I love you for who you are.

"*No.*" I interrupted myself. "Forget the word *love*. Since nobody knows what it means, maybe it should be banned from the books."

"You're bitter, Ed."

"Bitter? *I'm alive.* And those who say they love you, they do the most betraying. So I'll settle for *like*. I like you just fine as you are, Scott. I can only hope you'll go on liking me for who I am."

Scott thought about this for too long a time, then asked, "But what if I still feel uncomfortable about it? Should I be dishonest about that?"

"Dishonest? No, of course not. See?" I pointed to an absent third party. "See, Jerry? You're wrong."

"Wrong?" Scott's eyes darted about the shop. "Who's Jerry?"

"He's, uhhh, an old friend. But a little slow in coming round. Or maybe," I turned my pointing finger on myself, "could be it's me who's slow. So," my arm dropped and swung at my side, "do you think you can explain your discomfort? Then we can work on it together. Like friends."

"But what if I can't?" Scott's question faltered. "I can't explain it."

"Then that proves what I've suspected all along. You can't explain what's not your doing. It's coming from someplace else. I'd like to see you free of it."

"And what if—?" Now Scott became the time-traveller. "What if the only way I'll be free of it is by being free of you?"

The words struck at me hard, an iceberg unannounced meeting up with my weakest point. "But Scott," I flinched. "You need me."

"Need you. Why?"

I hunted among scraps of memory, recalled a Patrick favorite, and asked, "Have you ever heard Barbara Cook sing 'Carolina in the Morning'?"

"Don't think so." Scott looked puzzled. "I'm not sure I know Barbara Cook."

"There," I said, my lineage assured. "Were it not for Patrick, I might not have known either. And were it not for me—well, Barbara Cook originated the role of Cunegonde on Broadway. In *Candide*."

"*Candide*? That's a book. Read it in ninth grade, because I had to. Didn't get the point."

"They made it into a musical, too. Then a lot of people didn't get the point. Not at first. And Barbara Cook, she played Marian the Librarian. You know, *The Music Man*."

"I know *The Music Man*." Scott rolled his eyes. "The big parade. Seventy-six trombones. But I don't remember Marian the Librarian. Or, wait. Did she sing 'Till There Was You'?"

"The very one."

"Then I do—I do remember. But not Barbara Cook." Scott paused, then fancied. "I suppose she's beautiful."

Thinking of her plump frame, I winked to myself and said, "She has a pretty face."

Impatience now swept his features, and in ripple effect Scott raised his right sleeve with his left hand. "I really need to be going," he said, noting the time again on his wristwatch. "But I'll take that paperback dictionary."

Reminded of my duties, I picked up the bound copy of *The American Heritage Dictionary*, returned it to its place, then retrieved the smaller paperback version.

"Will this do?" I asked, offering the book to Scott.

"It will." He made a quick nod and took the book into his hands.

I walked over to the counter and rang up the sale on the register. Scott followed me.

"Twelve sixty-seven," I said. "Now we'll see if your Am Ex is still happy."

Scott shoved his hand into his pocket. "I think I can pay cash today," he said, pulling some loose bills from his slacks. He gave me a ten and two ones, then searched in a second pocket for change. He came up with a quarter and a nickel. "Sorry, I'm a little short."

"Don't worry about it. You brought me coffee. Keep the quarter. You never know when you might have to spend time at a Laundromat." I reached for the smaller coin. "But if you don't mind, I'll take that nickel. You'd be surprised how far a nickel can take you."

Scott put the nickel into my hand, and repeated: "You don't make any sense to me, Ed. And when I leave the shop today, I'll leave knowing who Barbara Cook is, but what difference will that make in my life?"

My head began its slow nod again, and hearing the words of Jerry's prophecy tolling, I resigned myself to the fate of a friendship foretold. It was sinking to the bottom of the ocean as surely as that ship said to be unsinkable, all subsequent schemes to raise and loot its strong boxes of countless nickels failing. Yet a dim figure lingers on deck, a chanteuse singing softly to herself:

> *Where the morning glories*
> *twine around the door,*
> *Whispering pretty stories*
> *I long to hear once more.*

I looked into the refuge of Scott's shirt, the white waves of the cotton cloth taking in my sadness. It held me for the briefest moment, like the hopeful loop of a life preserver in black waters. There among those perfect waves for the first time I saw a crease, beneath its sharp line a blue shadow the color of snow in moonlight, and I fixed on it. Seeing this, Scott must have begun a slow warming trend, as if he'd pulled up beside me in a lifeboat, and reconsidering his position, coaxed me on board.

"I'm having them boxed," I heard him say.

"My shirts," he answered, the smile breaking out into laughter. "I'm having them boxed."

"Oh, I see." I returned the smile. "Of course you are. Wouldn't want anyone to think..."

It would be the last time I'd see Scott's smile. The last time I would hear his laughter. We exchanged goodbyes and a parting handshake. Scott left the bookshop.

I returned to my coffee cup behind the counter. It was only a sip shy of full, but stone-cold, cold as that rock Sisyphus monotonously pushes up that mountain only to see it slide back down again.

I took the paper cup to the front of the shop and opened the heavy glass door. Pausing, I looked out toward the street as Scott's flashy blue car sped away toward Lanchester Pike, its driver invisible behind tinted glass. The car stopped at the light, waited for the signal to change, then made a left and disappeared. I walked out onto the pavement and hurled my cup into one of the trash cans Summitt municipality provides.

A young woman was coming up the walk, guided by a terrier on a leash. I took brief notice of the dog, then looked up at the woman. Eyes meeting, we both smiled as she tossed her golden hair in the morning light.

Pointing to the dog, I said, "That's a Scottie, isn't it?"

"He is," she confirmed with the same pride a fellow might take in his car. "He's a good guy."

The dog came to the trash can, sniffed at the ground, and lifted a leg.

"Popular spot," I said, eyeing the widening splash of urine, then the blonde's naked fingers. She giggled, and I added, "Don't get me wrong. I'm no matchmaker. I'm a bookseller."

Both dog and woman cocked their heads as I retreated to the bookshop.

WHEN I RETURNED to my Philadelphia apartment that evening, I remembered the letters I'd written to Nancy on those Sundays leading up to Patrick's death, the ones I'd called "On Not Being Able to Feel the Words of Buffy Sainte-Marie." Nancy had lent them to me the summer after the suicide, one year before I was to meet Scott. Then I'd intended to share them with Patrick's family, but never did. The writing had seemed poor, too personal and self-absorbed. Patrick's family, I felt, would find nothing in them to absolve their grief. But neither had I returned them to Nancy, so on this evening I went looking for them again.

Like Patrick's suicide note several years before, they'd found their way to the bottom of a pile. I pulled them out and began reading with renewed interest. To my surprise, there at the back of the letters were several pages I'd added that same summer Nancy had lent them to me. What I'd remembered as no more than a sketch dulled by sorrow was instead a clear account of the evening of his suicide. I include that addendum here.

On Not Being Able to Feel the Words of Buffy Sainte-Marie, Part Five, Or The Last of Patrick

So what are we but the story we keep repeating, editing, censoring, and embellishing in our heads? The self is not like the hero of a B-movie who remains unaffected by the storms of passion and intrigue that swirl around him from the opening credits to the end. The self is more akin to the complex and ambiguous characters who emerge, develop, and suffer across the pages of a novel. There is nothing thinglike about me at all. I am more like an unfolding narrative.

—Stephen Batchelor, *Buddhism Without Beliefs*

It is a great thing to die in your own bed, though it is better still to die in your own boots.

—George Orwell

WHEN THEY FOUND PATRICK, HE was neither in his own bed, nor did he have his boots on. He was lying on the hard pavement at the foot of our apartment building, my house of spirits, now plus one, and he was in his stockinged feet. Because they were sticking out of the white sheet they'd pulled over him, I saw the feet first and I recognized them, the way you would an old hat or pair of gloves broken in over time. One pair of stockinged feet may look much the same as another, but when you've lived with someone for eighteen years, you even come to know him by the odd detail. Still, I don't think it was his feet the detectives had in mind when they asked me to identify the body.

"Should we call his family and have them do this?" one of the detectives had asked me.

"No," I said. "Why bother the family with this tonight?" I recognized the deed for what it was, a colorless formality. I might just as well be identifying a clipped thumbnail. Resigned and duty-bound, I said, "I can do it."

In fact, I more than wanted to do it: I needed it done. But as much as anyone can know a thing, I already knew. The particular shape that white sheet had taken on. The silent empty apartment, its door uncharacteristically unlocked, as if the swiftly retreating occupant dared not pause to consider his exit. Patrick's last pack of cigarettes still on the end table next to his chair where he'd monotonously sat for much of the last three years of his life. The very day, May 12, 1997. A day after Mothers' Day, the very same day Patrick had promised me he would get help. And Patrick himself those last months and weeks, the details of what comprised a lifestyle being let go, one by one. All pointed to the body under the white sheet before anyone bothered to lift it.

In my shock, I was hardly aware why the detectives were there. They seemed like superfluous props belonging to someone else's play. But I dutifully answered the questions they put to me, and in a voice stunned into monotone, misspoke more than once. I said that when I came home that evening, I found the apartment door open, when it was merely unlocked. I put Patrick's age at thirty-six instead of forty-six, a not-so-odd slip since Patrick began to cease living about ten years before his actual death. When asked if I could establish my whereabouts at 5:15 that evening, I said that I would have been getting off the Suburban Express at Thirtieth Street Station. But then, remembering, I corrected myself. While waiting for the train at Summit Station, I'd heard an announcement over the P.A.—the train was running approximately ten minutes late. This meant that I would have still been on board at 5:15.

"When did you reach the apartment?" a detective asked.

"About six," I estimated, explaining that I'd picked up something for dinner while passing through Thirtieth Street Station. I'd then leisurely strolled home that mild day, pausing to greet my neighbors' dogs in Schuylkill Park. Reaching the alley that runs alongside of the apartment building, I'd turned up it, but was stopped cold. An emergency vehicle was backing down the alley, and a man standing at its side directed it with the circular wave of his arm. Seeing me, he put his right arm straight out, and with his flattened palm, commanded me to halt.

"This is a crime scene," he shouted. "Move back!"

But I craned my neck and continued forward, trying to ask the man in white what the nature of the crime was. My tongue had already dried in its place, the voice no more than a thought in a woozy head—or at best a whisper that could not be heard above the

"beeep"

"beeep"

"beeep"

of the back-up signal. I could see in the near distance yellow streamers strung like party decorations around the white-sheeted body, the already familiar stockinged feet protruding.

There was a police car beside it, the door on the passenger side hanging open, and a crowd of people formed a semi-circle around the two. How odd. All these people stuck like mannequins in sunlight, having so little to do but to gawk at a sheet under which there happened to be a body. Was some huckster collecting admission in anticipation of the unveiling? Yet I, who came up this same alley daily on my route home—I was being yelled at, waved away.

"Not this way," the man again commanded as I pushed closer, "that way."

"Wake up!" I wanted to bark back, not only to the man doing the directing, but to the whole crowd of assholes who'd apparently forfeited their admissions and snuck in ahead of me. "Get on with your own lives!" But my message would have been censored by the

    "beeep"

                      "beeep"

                                          "beeep"

of the back-up signal.

So I gave in to the command, backed off, and walked over to the next street, repeating the litany along the way: it was a crime scene I'd happened on, not a suicide. Never mind those familiar feet. Suicide is a private business, not a public spectacle. Patrick was comfortably ensconced before the television in our apartment, the evening news recounting the day's events. That semi-circle of people formed the upper curve of a question mark. Joe Nobody was under that white sheet.

But when I'd completed my alternate route, walking round to the front of the apartment building, I saw a woman whose face I knew but whose name I did not. She stood at the head of the alley, talking with another nameless neighbor. I couldn't make out a word she spoke, but a single gesture correctly diagnosed the situation. Her finger pointed to the top of the apartment building, and she drew a line in the air representing the trajectory of a fall. The finger stopped at the pavement below, taking dead aim at the body beneath the sheet. I could not yet bring myself to turn the corner and confront the thing up close. I needed to be sure that Patrick was not, as I imagined him, in the apartment above.

I entered the building, rode the elevator to the fifth floor, walked the length of the hall, and turned the knob of 5-C. The door opened without the aid of a key. The evening news did not blurt the day's events from the television. The silence instead informed me. Patrick's chair was empty. I went to his bedroom and passed beneath the arch of the open door. Patrick was nowhere within. I returned to the living room and walked over to the telephone on the end table next to Patrick's chair. Picking up the receiver, I dialed Patrick's sister. As the phone on the other end began to ring, I noticed the pack of cigarettes sitting on the end table and next to it the small framed photograph out of which looked Patrick, our friend Christie, and me. I took up the pack of cigarettes and flipped it open as the trio in the photograph witnessed the interrupted countdown: nine cigarettes remained. Patrick's sister answered her phone. Was Patrick there? I asked in a pleading voice. Had he been there earlier that day? Had he phoned for help? Was he on his way there now?

Patrick's sister was about as informed as an inmate in a Kafka story, and when my questions had run out, I told her to prepare for the worst.

"It's a beautiful day," she suggested, with a nonchalance that only confirmed her ignorance. "Patrick probably went out for a walk."

Patrick's sister didn't understand. In those last months her brother had been deprived of the simple pleasure of an afternoon stroll. I told Patrick's sister that I would phone her again as soon as I knew more.

"Yes," she said. "Call me the moment he gets back."

I hung up the phone.

I went to the kitchen and fiddled with the dinner I'd carried home. I optimistically put out two plates, the habit of eighteen years. The smell of the food turned my stomach. Abandoning the meal, I left the kitchen and went to the apartment door, opened it, and stared down the hall. The lighted exit sign at its end pointed ominously to the elevator and the fire escape landing beyond. I stepped back into the apartment, closed the door and leaned against it, the weight of my existence meant to shut out the inevitable. Going to the bathroom, I caught a glimpse of that guy in the mirror above the sink. Who was he?

Running a faucet, I splashed cold water onto the stranger's face, letting the features drip in would-be tears. It could be another minute passed, maybe five. My internal clock had gone haywire. I returned to the door of 5-C, opened it, and started down the hall toward the elevator, which yawned at my approach. Out sprang two men, each flashing a detective's credentials. One of them said there was a body outside. *Might I know whose it was?*

As if the word *body* in this context did not convey the precise meaning, I presumed the sex of the object in question and asked, "Is he dead?"

The two detectives exchanged a glance. Then one answered with an unmistakable finality, "Oh, yes."

I wanted to shove the two detectives back into the elevator, push the reverse button on the VCR, and rewind the day. But some days, some decisions, some turns of events cannot be undone. You can lose your money, borrow more, win or earn it back. You can quarrel with a friend, reconsider your position, and make up. You can break a dish, glue it, or go out and buy another.

But then there is this thing sudden beyond sudden. Absolute. Irreversible. No tantrum will get you your way. No prayer is loud enough to be heard. No finely worded apology will bring the absent friend back to this bargaining table. No lottery jackpot or stock dividend is large enough to buy out the competition. Time is that narrow precipice jutting out into thin air, and you have just taken a step too far.

I looked neither detective in the eye, but spoke to the space separating the two, saying, "I think I know who it is."

The battery of questions followed, each detective stabbing me with a measure of interrogation, then allowing the other his turn. Eventually one asked me if I could show them Patrick's room. I guided them into the apartment, led them beneath the arch of the doorway and the bedroom in question. There they did some unobtrusive snooping, explaining they were looking for some identification and a possible suicide note. I said I did not think there would be a note.

"How could you know that?" I was asked accusingly.

I awkwardly explained that Patrick and I had talked about suicide on several occasions. Patrick had said it was a myth that suicides left notes, that mostly they did not.

Turning the tables, I asked one of the detectives directly: "Is that true?"

"Sometimes there's a note," he answered. "Sometimes not. I don't have the data at my fingertips."

One of the detectives spotted Patrick's keys on his bureau. "Neither keys nor identification were found on the body," he said. "That kind of anonymity is unusual. Can you explain it?"

I thought a bit, then answered, "It's not so strange. Patrick didn't jump with any concern about being identified. He would probably have preferred to evaporate. And I don't think he'll be needing keys where he's going."

I noticed Patrick's passport near the keys on the bureau, pointing to it and saying, "He won't be needing that either."

One of the detectives retrieved the slender booklet and flipped it open to Patrick's picture. Looking at the photo, he said, "This could hardly be the man downstairs."

My eyes fairly popped, thinking perhaps that it was not Patrick's body on the pavement outside. But when the detective handed me the passport and I saw the photograph within, I recognized the confusion at once. It had been taken about ten years before, when Patrick and his family had gone to Europe. Perhaps that was his last good time. The man in the photo is handsome, tawny-skinned, clear-eyed, well groomed. A picture of health. Yet even in that healthy face, the clever camera had caught the crease of a shadow. I frowned, closed the passport, and handed it back to the detective. I was once again as certain as I have been of anything.

Patrick Jacob Scott Robinson, Jr., as his name is given on his passport, took his own life on the 12th of May, 1997, on account of unreasonable unhappiness. He had been like that man in the Stevie Smith poem:

> *I was much too far out all my life
> And not waving but drowning.*

"Did Patrick use hard drugs?" a detective asked.

"He seemed to get enough mileage out of booze and cigarettes," I answered.

"Had Patrick ever before attempted suicide?"

"Once before. That I knew of. Sometime in his late teens, early twenties. An overdose of pills, he'd told me. He took everything that was in the family medicine cabinet. They pumped him clean. But in a way his whole lifestyle became increasingly suicidal."

One of the detectives looked up at the picture of Jesus that hung on the wall above Patrick's bed. It's that familiar one based on the painting by Walter Sallman called "Head of Christ." The eyes are a little too blue. The long, wavy brown hair, bathed in a spiritual glow, is a little too light. The features are too pretty. A pretty face, if ever there was one. The perfect poster boy to attract followers. *My blond Jew*, I've come to calling him. Half a century ago, a reproduction like this one would have been found in almost any Catholic household. I'd bought it used from a thrift shop when Patrick and I had first moved into the city. One of the nickel and dime pictures of a poor man's art collection. Originally it had hung in our living room, but years later Patrick had put it over his bed. More recently still he'd suspended a strand of rosary beads from the top of the frame.

Noting both beads and picture, the detective asked, "Was Patrick Catholic?"

"He was," I answered, "though I don't know how much good it did him." I thought of Patrick's unsent letter to his parents, the one I'd taken from him and hidden in my room. Were I able to remember where I'd put it, I might have shown it to the detectives. But I hadn't looked for it in three years. It was probably in a book on a shelf. But which book, what shelf? I put it out of my mind.

"Was Patrick HIV-positive?"

"Don't think so. I'm not really sure. Once he said he was, later not. That it was, you know, a misdiagnosis." Confusion left me. "Patrick was alcoholic. He lied about the littlest things. I didn't know what was, what wasn't true."

"That's often the case in this kind of situation," one detective said. Then he asked, "Do you think you could identify the body?"

"Or should we call his family and have them do this?" asked the other.

I can do it, I insisted. I am man enough. Man I am, green eggs and ham.

"Did Patrick have financial problems?"

"I guess. He was surely headed for them. He was borrowing heavily from me. He'd quit his job without telling me. I heard about it a few months later from his sister."

"You didn't know?" the detective asked, astonished, having probably assumed what many may have assumed. "Weren't you close?"

"We weren't lovers," I said, "if that's what you mean. Not once, never did we..." My voice began to break up. "But there'd been a time when we were very close friends. Buddies all those years. Can't you picture it? At first it was easy for Patrick to pretend he was still going to work. Since my business is in the suburbs, his in the city, I leave in the morning before him, and come home in the evening after him."

The happy thought of Patrick cooking up a great dinner, its scent greeting me at the door after a long day, was shattered by a detective's admonishment. "But you continued to give him money? Even after you found out he'd quit his job and was hiding the fact?"

"What was I supposed to do?" I snapped back. "Leave him to starve? He was in trouble, *deep trouble*. And I was his friend. If you dropped every friend at a sign of trouble, you'd be left with no one, nothing."

The detective frowned, then asked, "What had been Patrick's job?"

"Bookseller. He was a bookseller. So am I." A smile touched my lips. "I can still see Patrick on a Saturday evening back, say, in the early eighties, soon after we'd moved into the city. We'd come home tired at the end of a busy week in our respective shops. We'd put a record on and would have a talk over a leisurely drink before dinner." An old-fashioned vinyl disc spun on its turntable in my head. "How I loved those times. The unwinding, the stories shared. Good things coming our way. And some Saturday nights, after dinner, we'd go out for a night on the town. It was fun, before AIDS. But I suppose that sort of thing is always fun when you're young and a Saturday night is full of possibilities. And as we'd dress for our evening out, Patrick, the bookseller, would prance around the apartment singing in the manner of Barbra Streisand: 'Someday they'll clamor for my grammar.' He was my own, my private star. Maybe that's what friendship is."

The detectives' smiles matched mine.

"And such good company. So much fun. Almost anyone who knew him will tell you that. Smart, too. Though not a snotty intellectual. Just the right kind of brightness. If only he'd found a better way to direct it." My smile vanished.

"But the drinking. It got more and more out of hand. The good things, they came undone. Then both the two major bookstore chains opened near Patrick's shop. The business was clobbered. It didn't help."

"I would imagine not," one of the detectives sympathized.

I noticed the copy of *Kitchen Table Wisdom* I'd left out for Patrick to read the week before. It was sitting on top of a pile of dirty laundry. I went over to it, picked it up, and saw that the note I'd written and the agreement I'd had Patrick sign were still in it.

"Patrick tried to go cold turkey last week," I explained to the detectives. "Thursday, Friday, or Saturday, I guess. I'd lent him this book by Rachel Naomi Remen, my favorite chapters marked. I hoped the power of the stories would trigger something in him. Apparently they did.

"When I came home from work on those days, Patrick was in his room, the door shut. He'd left me notes saying he wasn't well, had a bug, and was trying to sleep it off. I didn't realize what he was attempting until after the fact, when he came out of his room on Saturday evening. He looked half dead, pale, shaking, the copy of *Kitchen Table Wisdom* in hand.

"'I loved these stories, Ed,' he said, holding the book above his head. 'And I love you.' The same hand dropped defeatedly. 'But I have to have one more bottle,' he pleaded, forcing back tears. 'Just one more bottle.'

"What could I do? I gave him the money for what turned out to be his last bottle."

I handed one of the detectives the copy of *Kitchen Table Wisdom*, saying, "In this high-tech world a lot of people seem to forget the power of the written word. I never can." And looking up again at the face of Jesus above Patrick's bed, I added, "I guess both Patrick and I were guilty of the same thing—stuck on a pretty face and the written word."

As the detective took the book into his hands, he pulled the yellow sheet of paper that jutted from its pages and unfolded it. Clearing his throat, he read aloud the hand-printed words of the agreement:

> I WILL CALL MY FAMILY ON MONDAY. I WILL GET HELP. I WILL ADMIT I HAVE PROBLEM. I MUST CHANGE. I AM NOT A BAD PERSON. I JUST SCREWED UP.
>
> *Patrick*

Listening to the words, I saw Patrick as he'd been just two nights before, the same document shaking in hand. He'd read it, took up my ballpoint pen, and dashed off his jagged signature. I'd then given him ten dollars, a tiny sum, saying, "This is in trust."

We'd hugged, the bond of our trust already broken, and what I felt I held in my arms was a skeleton.

The detective returned my yellow page to the copy of *Kitchen Table Wisdom*, then laid the book back on the pile of dirty laundry, suggesting it was time to go downstairs. He put his arm around me while the second detective led the way. We left the apartment, walked the length of the hall, and rode the elevator down to the street—a trio of travelers about to confront a dead star.

Reaching the alley, I saw that the police car with two policemen in it remained. The crowd that surrounded the body had grown from a crescent moon to something of a mob. One of the policemen got out of the car and began talking to a woman. The woman, I saw, was Leigh, whose family owns my house of spirits. She lives with her children in the apartment directly below 5-C. I tried to call out her name, but again I found it impossible to raise my voice above a crusty whisper. On my third or fourth "Leigh," she turned from the policeman and our eyes met. Later she would tell me she'd had no idea whose body it was under that white sheet, but the moment she looked into my eyes, she'd known.

"Leigh. I'm sorry," I said. "I'm sorry this had to happen here."

She continued to look into my eyes, her own now smitten in sorrow, and said, "I'm sorry for you."

I turned to the policeman and said that I was Patrick's friend and that I was here to make an identification. I asked one of the detectives if he could lift the white sheet for me, and that he should do it very slowly. I was thinking about the possible condition of the face. Would the skull be split? An eye outside the socket? Had Patrick dived head-first to be doubly sure of an instant death?

The detective expressed concern about the presence of children in the crowd. In response, the policeman who'd been talking with Leigh forced everyone, young and old, to back off—King Suddhodana protecting all the little buddhas.

Moving in closer, I crossed the yellow borders that marked the crime scene until I stood directly over the white sheet. Two detectives and a policeman followed. Just a few feet away I noticed a familiar pair of glasses resting on the pavement. One of the lenses was missing, the other cracked and glistening with afternoon sun.

"Those are Patrick's glasses," I said, pointing to the small rectangular frames. Like the stockinged feet there may be ten thousand duplicate pairs, but they were unmistakably his, the second eyes of my oldest friend.

The detective bent down toward the body and took up a corner of the sheet in his hand. He lifted it with care, slowly revealing the head, the face, the slight body. The skull was intact, the eyes shut. A few lines of already dried blood had meandered across the forehead and cheek. I didn't have to look but for that nanosecond.

"That's Patrick," I said, and turned away.

IN 1990, A WRITER OF exceedingly popular fiction enjoyed another enormous success with the tale of a wealthy businessman who opens a theme park populated with genuine dinosaurs. These dinosaurs, so the story goes, had been cloned from DNA extracted from insects who'd ingested the blood of those same dinosaurs more than one-hundred thirty-five million years before, only to find themselves entombed in amber shortly thereafter. It is a wonderful premise for a story. Something secreted from childhood and sunk deep in the craw of even the most cynical adult causes him to pause at the thought and ask of himself, "Could that be possible?" All this lively, once-upon-a-time sucking up cut down in its prime, each tiny carcass encased like Snow White in her translucent coffin, then to thaw these hundreds of millennia later. And finally, with only a kiss of ancient data, to resuscitate a line of long-extinct giants, their presence to reinvigorate the very concept of a summer carnival. The suggested kernel of science therein allows the tale to rise above the genie flowing from the lamp or the wizard found at the end of a long yellow road. Never mind that I know more marriages end in divorce than follow through till death us do part. So what that I know the life expectancy of a man cannot probably be pushed far beyond the one-hundred and twentieth year. Put aside the thought that the half-life of a radioactive substance may be as much as thirty thousand years, or that half the medicines in my bathroom cabinet have already expired and belong in the dumpster. And forget that I know the message of that parable about the wizard is that he did not grant the seekers who came to him either wit or pluck or heart and home. They needed only the encouragement of that authority showing the way: each already possessed what he'd deluded himself he lacked.

So never mind that I know no matter how thick the amber brick embalming those insects might be, no active ingredient can remain so after the passage of one-hundred thirty-five million years. I prefer to let what's left of the child in me believe in the story he is about to hear: the ride is the thing—there is no other.

But though I know each life to be an individual clock that revs up, reaches a crescendo, then winds down, I also know, or sense, that some remnant of that timepiece is invariably passed along. It may come in the form of living offspring, there to carry on a name and the hope of a family business. Or as real estate, a fattened will and securities, or the pretty stuff of dreams: antique silver, a painting, a table with its chairs. Or even something simple as the tick, tick, ticking of a story begun on borrowed yellow sheets and streaked in tears, retold, then sent uninsured through the mails. The brain secretes its own amber gel and floats her dinosaurs in a private Labrea Pit. And such a story privately begun can come to reach outward like the light of an already dead star crossing a night sky. No single Magellan can live long enough to make such a crossing. No single storyteller can bring the thing to conclusion. The task must be handed down, moved along, let go, and reworked by the hands of yet another generation and another. So whether by genetic transmission, a living will, money kept in a sock and left between bedsprings, a passion play, a love story—all these become the interchangeable pieces of a puzzle not created so much for its solving, but whose reading can only be found in the act of living.

Henceforth, the sign above the bookshop door ought to read:

BOUND MATTERS
ONLY LIVE

Part Three

This last portion of the text is dedicated to the living memory of Helen Clovis. Reader of children's books, reader of adult novels that do not flinch at any part of the human experience. In short, a reader par excellence.

Reaching the shop the next morning, I saw that Scott had returned my letters. Not a third set of copies, but the entire cast of originals. Each group of yellow sheets was tucked neatly back into its envelope, their refrain mocking me tenfold:

> How Scott Aaron Matthews...
> How Scott Aaron Matthews...
> How Scott....

The words had been flung on hard pavement before the shop door, no white-sleeved arm or cup of coffee in warming accompaniment, more like the baby Moses sent floating among watery reeds. Even without reading the note Scott included in the abandoned packet, I sensed what this meant. Jerry's prophecy had come to pass.

Just as Patrick had leapt to an abrupt death, the guillotine had fallen on my union with Scott, its once flame-retardant core burned beyond recognition. The friendship was done, and it was done differently from any other I'd seen ended. There'd be no record, not the smallest memento in Scott's life that I had ever been there. And this was no natural parting of ways, but a surgery radical as amputation. Growth hadn't required it. To the contrary: growth ended there, the upshot of Scott's note being that I should not contact him—*ever again*. It read like a threat, as if the warm handshake I'd grown accustomed to had been replaced by a clenched fist wagging in the air above his head. But however harsh the wording, however tight that fist and perfect the vacuum within—whatever the outward manifestation—I understood this was not the genuine Scott, but an imposter. The ghost that would haunt me hence wasn't veiled in white, but donned a busy patchwork, would fumble, then follow through on the script Jerry knew only too well, the Scott Jerry hadn't even met but whose ultimate act he could rightly predict. This loose-ended Scott was part Patrick leaping to his death, part Jeff egging me on to San Francisco then dropping me there, part every straight man whose open friendship I'd longed for but whose closeness we together feared.

Gone was the strong Scott I'd held in my arms. Lost was the courageous Scott who'd boldly reprinted a lengthy, intricately personal letter sent to him by another man. And lost, too, was the playful Scott who laughed with me as our fanciful honeymoon wound to conclusion. Like Patrick striking hard pavement, the old Scott had shattered and was as good as dead. In his place was something hollow, a plastic Mr. Potatohead where once had been the sweet flesh of a vine-ripened fruit. My friend first-born of a trinity of yeses wasn't a mail-order mate acting out a catalogue's hype, but a human being who felt deeply and saw clearly. Through what chute in this jungle of snakes and ladders had he chosen to exit? And what had I done to be so abruptly orphaned?

I've known divorces where one spouse was forbidden to see another, this where abuse had been proven, or a child's safety called into question. But with physical contact confined to handshakes and two hugs, no child could come of this union. There had been a friendship forged in confusion, but I'd deliberately kept a distance from Scott, never went to his place of business, hadn't once knocked on his front door. I'd even turned down the offer to join him in his confounded reading group, effectively reducing three-thousand three-hundred pages to a single sour note. And while it was Scott who'd happened into my life, now I was being forbidden contact with his—*ever again*. Consecutive life sentences for Henderson and McKinney would amount to no less.

The cold blade that fell on the nape of my neck that morning separated mind from heart, the split clean as debris departing a world that's stopped spinning. I stumbled aimlessly about the shop, a horseless version of that denizen of Sleepy Hollow, the fallout of faded fig leaves heralding the season. I would be given a pumpkin with chiseled features for a face, store-bought pie filling for brains. When in the course of "ever again" the pumpkin should rot, I would find another at *Fresh-as-a-Daisy Field* and chisel a new set of frozen features. Then another and another. It would be as tiresomely repetitive as that Sisyphus story, pumpkin shells instead of rock, the mush of pie filling oozing from Vesuvius' crater. And Ichabod Crane cowering there in the status quo—as big a wimp as ever.

We die. Not once, not finally, but several times over in the course of a lifetime. When I was in my early teens and my parents separated, I died for the first time. Childhood was finished, and I took to the refuge of story books and the writing of poems. I died again when I found myself alone in San Francisco, a place beautiful and strange to the unsophisticated soul of a country boy. My bound companions there, nurturing and buffering, were Rainer Maria Rilke and a biography of Gertrude Stein. I died again, finding myself in a gentleman's profession in Philadelphia. Family life, a love life, an economic future—each way seemed blocked to me. But like a hapless Brer Rabbit hurled into a thorny brier, there in Philadelphia I was able once more to take refuge in stories found in books. The gathering grew to include Flannery O'Connor, Henry Miller, Saul Bellow, Vladimir Nabokov, poets Arthur Rimbaud and W.H. Auden, as well as that kingfish Proust. With *The New Yorker* I learned to appreciate the nervous mutts of George Booth, with the Sunday *New York Times* to stalk Ninas in the ink foliage of an Al Hirschfeld.

Yet again I died with Patrick gone, and for a time that abrupt end sent me into a numbing silence no story could reach. The rumor still haunting my house of spirits is that Patrick slipped from the fire escape landing. "Accidental fall" I've heard murmured in the hall. But it was no accident. He was pushed from long ago, another domino in response to another domino, not looking backward to ask where the push had come, not looking forward to tell where it might lead. And though I was miles away, riding a train toward his conduct unbecoming, my hand was there pushing, too. It is one of those thoughts, worn out by the weight of its own truth: in silence there is consent, so that by not siding with a solution, in passivity you become indistinguishable from the problem.

This morning, too, I died. I'd left my silent retreat when Scott happened into my life, and in that fertile, star-crossed moment, conception occurred.

Did I say there'd been no child? I was mistaken. Never have I been more mistaken. Ghosts of countless sperm may litter my bed sheets, but a lone fighter survived. And whether labeled bastard, love child, dividend or accident, it was a bundle of joy that struck hard pavement before the shop door. So what if Jerry had rightly predicted this affair's final act? He could not anticipate the sequel coming from what was left adrift. It was time for the baby Moses to grow up and, by the power vested in him, to part those bloody waters. In that abandoned packet of letters there remained but a single story to tell:

my own.

I had begun that story by opening my heart to a man who was ill-prepared to take in all he was being told. I would bring it to conclusion by opening my heart to the world. And unlike another distant, less frequent flier, I would face up to this inappropriate sun—and hold fast to the hope of my feathers.

The pang beginning in that morning's sickness requires little more than a footnote. I had entered the year working out a single loss; I would leave it with two. I pleaded with some friends to play go-between and contact Scott so that he might reconsider his position. If reconciliation was too much to ask, then we could at least have a final talk and a formal goodbye. No one would comply. Some saw my request as an invasion of Scott's privacy. Others suggested I was behaving like a child pursuing a relationship where none was desired. But like that piece of John Cage music, the question of desire remained unanswered—was created unanswerable. Were it otherwise, expressions of longing would have been spent just outside

Eden's gate. Instead, they move on, unhampered and self-renewing, almost as though they'd never existed before.

Fortunately the bookshop remained to occupy me, and though I went through the motions of my routine as if sleepwalking, the movement was forward still. Best I could, I put aside thoughts of rewriting until after the holiday season passed. I did, however, find myself doing some preliminary research, and on a breezy Sunday afternoon, stopped in at the local gay bookshop in Philadelphia. This busman's holiday was spent combing the stacks for material concerning relationships between gay and straight men. About all I found were implausible sexual encounters, all of these, presumably, pure fantasy, since consensual sex between two adult men at least implies the orientation of the said straight man has been called into question. It wasn't explicit details I was looking for, but something infinitely more subtle, perhaps impossible to put to page. If busman's holiday this was, I might have had a better time at a shop whose theme was not a sexual orientation, but a spiritual one.

Sadly, too, I discovered that Betsy's claim that the gay male remains among the highest at risk for suicide of any group in the population is not mere speculation. Rates of addictions, teen runaways, and depressive disorders are also disproportionately high. These sorry numbers, so easily documented, all belong to a status quo whose maintenance I wanted no part in.

And though sexual preference is increasingly thought to have a biologic or genetic base, even my limited research made it clear that negatives haunting same-sex preference continue to be largely societal in origin. Not a response to homosexuality itself, but to attitudes toward it. Self-acceptance alone—indeed the whole of the gay and civil rights movements—had done nothing to push down that suicide rate. The reach that would begin to point to real change would need to come from outside the gay community.

I have long thought that where sexual orientation is concerned, the genetic link, however likely, is not the important thing. We've always known that skin color has to do with who our biological parents happen to be, but this knowledge alone has not been responsible for the weakening of racial tensions or the elimination of racism. It took a President with the courage of Harry S Truman to integrate the armed forces, a leader with the charisma of Dr. Martin Luther King, Jr. to awaken the nation.

The odd thing about sexual orientation in regard to the armed forces is that gay people are already well dispersed and sifted into that whole—as they continue to be in every aspect of society, whatever the prevailing mood. In fact I would say there is not a more evenly distributed minority. But tucked within this integration there remains a cruel irony: gay people are still too often asked to be silent about what in every other instance is regarded as a virtue—the capacity to love. And further, to swallow a pride so frequently misshaped in adolescence, to remain the truly invisible men and women.

There are discrepancies in our being—*diversity demands it.* Some stem from birth, some we begin acquiring at a later date. The best are gained in time by sheer effort. What needs tracing and describing is not so much the source of these differences but what among them passes for conscience. Throw that into sunlight, and the discrepancies will lose their importance. The negatives will then gradually slip away.

AMONG THE EXTENDED family members of my Wisconsin childhood there'd been an uncle named Emil. He'd worked on the railroad, was a handyman, an expert carpenter, and would probably have been more expert still had he not liked his whiskey so well. But he is best remembered by me for his small arsenal of mostly poor jokes repeatedly told. Whenever whiskey got the better of him, those already overworked stories took a turn for the worse—as eventually so did Uncle Emil.

One of his jokes tells the story of two workmen sharing a bench at lunchtime. Each opened his lunchbox, and from within one of them pulled a limp sandwich. Separating the twin slices of white bread, he peered at the contents and grumbled, "Not peanut butter and jelly again."

Pulling a chicken leg from his lunchbox, the other workman asked, "Why don't you tell your wife to make something different?"

"Don't bring my wife into this," the first workman snapped back. "I made this sandwich."

There is little more that needs to be added to my story. Absent at this point is a letter written to Katharine, Scott's girlfriend in the early autumn of 1998. Through an odd turn of events we happened to meet on the morning of Christmas Eve that same year. I learned then that Scott and Katharine had talked about my letters and the motives behind their composition. They'd disagreed. Katharine made the case that I was attempting to enlighten Scott on some issues; Scott felt he wasn't in need of enlightening. After all, he'd nothing against gay men, and had no desire to cramp their lifestyles. Further, Scott argued, if I'd been a woman coming on to him and he'd not shared the attraction, he would have been equally put off. But Katharine countered that I was neither a woman, nor had I actually come on to Scott. And since homophobia does not directly accompany the relationship between a man and a woman, how could the bond between two men, whatever the degree of intimacy, be said to be precisely the same? The debate escalated, the topic finally dropped, not to be broached again.

Once the busy holidays had passed and I settled into the routine of working out the book, I wrote Katharine at her new home in San Francisco, thanking her for efforts made on my behalf. This connection to Scott's former companion, and to the city I'd left more than two decades before, momentarily relieved my sense of isolation. But the link was to prove fleeting, my letter unanswered.

In the year to come, I also managed to track down Scott's longtime companion Amy, who had moved to New England. I wrote her about my project, a book in which both she and her ex-fiancé were characters. Amy responded immediately, eager to hear more. I gladly sent her an early draft, partially typed, part hand-written in the mirror image of her own script. Amy's curiosity, however, must have soured at her reading, for she failed to respond a second time. Again my hopes for a sustained connection quickly faded.

I next consulted lawyers. My initial concern had been with issues of privacy. If the book were completed and published, would the terrain and the people who populated it be too recognizable? Upon reading a draft similar to that one I'd sent Amy, one of these lawyers advised that since there was no malice in my portrayals, I should not worry about repercussions. Still, I was anxious, and suggested to this lawyer that I might set up a small trust for Scott's firstborn as a show of good will and compensation for any further discomfort the publication of the book might cause. At this, the lawyer vigorously shook his head, saying I should give up any thought of contact with Scott. His feelings had been made clear, and if I did not follow Scott's dictum and keep a distance, I could be accused of stalking. *Stalking?* Had this lawyer read the same book I believed I'd composed? The notion of a stalker conjures up a John Hinckley in leering pursuit of a Hollywood star, the outcome an assassin's bullet temporarily shattering another more complacent Presidency. How could someone liken that Star Wars scenario to the scant hope of a trust fund? Yet someone had.

And while Scott's feelings may have seemed clear to a legal mind, they remained muddied in my own. Or did they? Scott, in his odd complicity, had encouraged the book by reprinting my letters. Were he a closeted gay man, as Jerry had proposed, he would never have done this—multiplying, in effect, the evidence of the possibility threefold. But had Scott been your average straight guy, he would probably also have failed to follow through in this way. Scott could only be Scott. Neither the "fire of my loins," as Lolita was to a redundant Humbert Humbert, nor the friend of twenty years whose company I'd assumed until that moment of his abrupt departure. Instead, Scott would remain a promise

—neither kept nor broken—

but held in suspended animation, a hairsbreadth above all the rest.

Yes, Scott's feelings had been made clear. He'd never shared a sexual thought with another man, and could not be "in love" with me. But neither had he entirely shunned what I could only suppose was love. He'd embraced a gay man; out of mutual respect and without either having compromised his orientation, two men had embraced one another. It was an act of love that said as much, maybe more, than the grinding of body parts ever could, and it should have aroused a legal mind to the true call of my story. I had not given up my seat, and together Scott and I had moved a little forward.

Katharine's silence. Amy's interest rising, then falling. A dictum a lawyer suggested I must honor. All responses to a situation that had borne a book still in process and confirming what I had long suspected: it is far easier to begin the telling than it is to bring a story to satisfactory conclusion. And unlike my uncle's repeated stories, I would have but one opportunity to tell my tale.

It may be creation is indifferent to the fate of her children. Those lines threading stars in a night sky to form a constellation, they're yet another example or our seeing the universe not as it is, but as we are. What shines there isn't a ram, a pair of fishes, or a Greek hero, but our wishes.

And how should it be otherwise? The arbitrary line bringing design to abstraction isn't made by an ungrateful child who spites the indifference with his own creation. It is as likely drawn by that portion of God found in each of us. So I am returned to the role of solitary traveler, but with an attendant hope: that one day Scott would read my completed manuscript, connect the dots flung so far afield—and understand.

How Scott Aaron Matthews Can Change Your Life, Coda

I was perhaps in the second grade and surely a fledgling in regard to the English language. In those days in that small town of Brule, Wisconsin (town and river shared the name), two grades occupied a single classroom governed by one teacher. First and second grades under Miss Willowby, third and fourth under Miss Andersen, and so on. How a single teacher managed two entire grades I don't remember.

But how, I'd like to know, does a teacher manage even a single student? That the latter has been likened to a lump of clay in the hands of the former hardly holds under scrutiny, for clay remains clay no matter the shape. Better compare it to that other impossible profession, parenting, with matching hours and pay scale, and no union to address grievances. Or, best of all, rank it with love in any format—there being only one true direction: forward.

English was not my chosen language, but since that is what the natives spoke, that is what I was taught. Except for a few Finnish curse words and a couple of years of high school Spanish (*uno, dos, tres*—I can still count to ten on a clear day), I received no alternative language skills, and my affair with English was to prove as rocky as any other.

Thankfully our stories in second grade had risen quickly beyond Dick and Jane to something on a more sophomoric level. Though I was not so the sophomore to imagine myself ready for Marcel Proust, I knew from first-grade experience that Dick and Jane were a bore. Even with the introduction of a dog and younger sister, matters failed to improve. The plots were so thin they should have had a separate booth at the summer carnival where, for a quarter, you could step behind a large, hand-painted canvas panel whose captions were similar to the abbreviated reviews on book jackets:

"Amazing"

"Alive"

"See it to believe it."

Admission forfeited, you were then allowed to gawk at the likes of a man with two faces, the lizard boy, or the fat lady. It is a recurrent theme in both life and stories that the banner out front does not paint an accurate picture. The man with two faces didn't really have two faces, but had one head with half a face disfigured so that if you squinted it could be construed as a second set of features. The lizard boy didn't have scales and a forked tongue and tail, but was a short guy with lousy skin whose repair would deprive him of a living wage. The fat lady, it is true, turned out to be fat, but why pay a quarter for something you can get on the street for nothing? In short, most of what was advertised turned out to be less than the copy reported, but when you have spent the rest of your summer herding cows and putting up hay, dropping a quarter for even the chance at seeing something different is a risk you take.

And there were other diversions. A fun house, a spook house, a roller coaster and tilter-wheel, scantily clad girls in a row, a strong man. Or to test your own strength you could take a mallet to the base of a measuring rod and attempt to sound the bell at the top. Watching so many try and fail at this gong show, it came to me that the device was rigged so that no one's skill took him higher than the human degree of ninety-eight point six. But for booty never gained, the hope of consolation reappeared at each successive booth along the midway. And when you grew hungry, you could partake of a mutation known as the foot-long hot dog (though he, too, fell shy of the mark), and that gawd-awful stuff called cotton candy. Spun magically out of a silver cylinder onto a paper cone, its pastel resin would stick to the hand, then disappear in unqualified sweetness on the tongue. But there is something about a boy, a summer's day, and a carnival that makes even a thing like cotton candy a wonder.

I remember risking my nickels there by flinging them onto this large wooden floor upon which there was laid a grid of Lucky Strike insignias—maybe two hundred one way, then half as many the other. The inner circle of that logo containing the tobacco brand name was exactly the size of a nickel, and the object was to hurl and land it precisely so that the nickel would eclipse the name. I saw hundreds of nickels thrown, my own included, but I never witnessed a total eclipse and a payoff. When the floor was sufficiently covered with ill-matched coins, one of the carnies would come along with a wide push broom and make a quick killing. Though at a nickel a pop the gratuity was small, they'd been tossed with such abandon that no janitor ever made better tips. Each passerby would tally his lucky stars and take a chance. For some, the single nickel lost would prove like a drink set before an alcoholic, revealing the gambler in an otherwise conservative lot. I saw whole paper rolls of nickels broken and sprayed onto that wooden floor, this at a place in time where two dollars earned you a good meal in a respectable restaurant. And what was your reward if you actually made a lucky strike? You didn't get even one of your nickels back; rather a ceramic horse whose stomach held a ticking clock, or a Kewpie doll who was a cuter though no less rotund version of that fat lady you'd laid your quarter down before. More likely, you'd come away with a trinket you could've gotten free with your Cracker Jack. So you might rightly guess that the carnival brought out the Cracker Jack in us all, for it came to me with the passing of my childhood years how each summer game had been rigged. But I'd say we went willingly, even joyously, leaving nickels and quarters lighter than the thinnest man. Now I wish ten dollars or twenty, not two, could buy just one chance at happiness on a summer day. And I would say, as

Proust might, that a chance at happiness is equal to the prize, and ultimately more instructive than a time-telling horse.

In Summitt, Pennsylvania, you can get an imported chocolate wrapped in colored paper for two dollars. Or a fancy coffee drink for three. Jack's chili is a bargain at a dollar eighty-six, though some of Barbara's cheeses run well over ten dollars a pound—dear for someone raised on homegrown Wisconsin Colby. The movie theater with the old deco front has recently reopened as a quintuplex, meaning you can make your film selection from a menu of five. You can eat Chinese, Japanese, French, or Italian—the list goes on. And, of course, for sixty-four dollars you can purchase three-thousand, three-hundred odd pages of *Remembrance of Things Past*, though I would still recommend that you begin at twelve dollars with *Swann's Way*.

But where have I gotten to? In second grade, no matter what two-dollar delicacy was on the restaurant menu, my order was the same: a burger with fries. Which is why Old McDonald is a billionaire while those of us pushing Proust limp along.

So having graduated Dick and Jane, though not seasoned enough to appreciate Marcel, I found the stories we read in second grade began to gain complexity, their vocabulary swelling beyond the four-letter word. One day in class a six-letter word, *valley*, appeared in a story for the first time. I'd heard it spoken often enough, but had never contemplated a precise meaning. Perhaps Miss Willowby saw the question mark rise in my face, for she mercilessly pointed to my desk and asked for a definition. Now the heat was on. I slipped into deep thought.

Late on Friday afternoons at the old Brule School, a half hour before weekend dismissal, all eight grades would pour out of their four classrooms. A gangly, upright piano would be rolled into place, and Miss Olson of the fifth and sixth grades would provide accompaniment as we engaged in communal *singing in the hall*. It was often the high point of my week. One of the songs we'd routinely sing was "Red River Valley." I thought of this as before, the river water not figuratively red or tinted by the presence of some ore, but blood red as if Moses and God had teamed again to play another trick on those idolizing Egyptians.

Closer to home, I thought of the Brule River, the way it had sliced a deep path with steep embankments on its road to Lake Superior. The farmhouse where I lived was nearly a mile away, but on a still morning through the open window of my second-story bedroom, you could hear the water pounding on the rocks beneath, slicing ever deeper into the earth.

So it was with these twin images in mind, and without the aid of *The American Heritage Dictionary*, that I cleared my throat and boldly put forth my definition:

"A valley is a hill that goes down."

The classroom kept its silence for another moment, and then my unintended joke brought down the house. Miss Willowby, who seldom laughed, was first to do so, the entire student body following her lead in peals slow to subside. I understood dimly, if at all, what everyone thought was so funny. But I have never forgotten the immediate response to what seemed to me to be a perfectly legitimate definition. Not only is a valley a hill that goes down, its corollary is equally legitimate: a mountain is a valley that goes up. Now I can better see that both valley and mountain go up and down proportionately, and that which of those ways you happen to be moving depends upon your starting point. Further, I can see that we may start at such different places it's a wonder we find ground to meet peaceably at all.

But we do. If time, memory, and nickels lost have conspired to make you cynical, recall that there were some golden days in September and October of a year toward century's end when two unlikely candidates momentarily called themselves friends.

For those whose passage on earth is a comfortable stroll, it may be their dream to one day walk the moon. But my "star report" ends by pulling me back from those distances. I prefer to take my small steps here, where each side of the freak show canvas comes to resemble the other. And I would wed my hopeful baby steps to yours, the grid upon this floor like those dark footprints laid upon a pale tile, there to aid in the learning of a new dance step. And just above that grid and the forward motion of the dance itself, a song exerts a simple melody, the whisper of its lyric growing stronger each day:

*"Next time that friendship will go better,
next time that friendship will go better."*

So laugh, if you need, but don't disapprove of my youthful definition. I have been deepening valleys and riding mountains ever since. I invite you to do the same.

Begin.

Author's Note

The question has been put to me: is this story fact or fiction? The answer can be found in the telling, and is clearly stated at the end of the two scenes involving Jerry on pages 135 and 136.

This is a true story. Some dialogue has been devised and smoothed for the sake of narrative flow, and a couple of scenes are composites. Reality cannot be transcribed directly to the page. The result would be like that definition of a bore: he tells everything.

That each of us is sexually drawn to some persons and not to others is a situation every reader experiences. That we are sometimes inappropriately aroused is also a part of that ball of wax figuring into the human condition.

In the book, I have tried to give equal weight to all attractions, all intimacies. My hope is that no one will read into it that the story means to be a license to pursue any relationship, sexual or otherwise, not involving mutual consent.

But as for a label, I wish this document would not need one. It is a tale in transition hung up somewhere between fact and fiction—there to shed light on its whole and the free expression of all honest bonds. In portraying the dangers of invisibility, it is also meant as a plea for the legalization of same-sex unions. *Defense of Marriage* has meaning only where the right has been denied. And since each family—extended if not immediate—contains gay members, the more their visibility increases, the stronger those families will become.

Acknowledgments

I would especially like to thank those early readers who took the time to write up commentary when the material was far from satisfactory. Among these: Donna Miller, Anne Dalke, Jane Spencer, Pat Finley, Phil Wallis, Betsy Hesser, Julia and Happy Shipley, Francoise Parier, Ann Strong, Al Williams, and Stu Bernstein. Their remarks helped me to see where I had gone astray. A heartfelt toast to Tom Gibbons, his playwright's ear, and the joys of imperfection.

    Best regards to Vivien Hoke, who typed until she could type no more, and to Ann Miller, who picked up where Vivien left off, and who knows where the commas go.

Two or three things I know for sure and one of them is that telling the story all the way through is an act of love.

—Dorothy Allison